Richard Lacey has been Professor of Clinical Microbiology at the University of Leeds since 1983, a post which involves responsibility for infection control for the Leeds Western Health Authority. A graduate of Cambridge University, he is a Fellow of the Royal College of Pathologists and gained his doctorate from the Faculty of Medicine at the University of Bristol. He began his career at the London Hospital, where he gained his Diploma in Child Health, moving on to Bristol Royal Infirmary and the Department of Microbiology of the University of Bristol. For nine years he was Consultant in Infectious Diseases for the East Anglian Regional Health Authority. A frequent lecturer abroad, he has published articles in many scientific journals covering antibiotics, and bacteria and microorganisms.

RICHARD LACEY

Unfit for Human Consumption

Food in Crisis – The Consequences
of Putting Profit Before Safety

Grafton

An Imprint of HarperCollins*Publishers*

Grafton
An Imprint of HarperCollins*Publishers*
77–85 Fulham Palace Road,
Hammersmith, London W6 8JB

Published by Grafton 1992
9 8 7 6 5 4 3 2 1

First published in Great Britain by
Souvenir Press Ltd 1991

ISBN 0 586 09230 7

Set in Palatino

Printed in Great Britain by
HarperCollinsManufacturing Glasgow

TO FIONNA

Acknowledgements

Some of the material in this book was performed or researched by two colleagues, Dr Kevin Kerr and Dr Stephen Dealler; to both I say thank you.

The first draft was written in almost indecipherable long hand scribble. My secretary, Mrs Hilary Mobbs, has done a magnificent job in converting this into prose.

Contents

List of Figures and Tables

Introduction

In the developed countries of the world, most people expect to live to the age of 70 or more. The control of infectious diseases, improvements in the environment and in nutrition have all played important parts in achieving our longevity. Whilst argument continues over exactly what constitutes the ideal diet, we do know that the effects on our health of what we eat may not be apparent for many decades. The single most common fatal illnesses of middle and old age remain coronary heart disease and strokes and the earliest manifestations can occur in childhood. Thus our present lifespan is partly attributed to the nature of our diet many years ago—that is, to before the time of intensive rearing of many food animals and before the advent of moist food processing.

It is because it takes so long for the possible detrimental effects of what we eat to become apparent that there is so much uncertainty over the ideal diet. Rather, it is easier to relate our current food intake to our present state of health. And of course, many problems do seem to occur soon after eating contaminated food. The estimated number of food poisoning cases per year in the United Kingdom is now approximately one million. By and large, these have been well publicised and understood. It is, however, the longer term risks from present methods of food preparation that are much less tangible. The easy attitude is to deny the existence of any long-term risk from new technology, since the problems may not be detected for decades.

For example, the extent of the dangers of chemicals applied to cereals, vegetables, potatoes, rice and fruit cannot be defined. However, we can be confident that they are in themselves most unlikely to confer any benefit on the consumer. The area of pesticides and agrochemicals as a whole is outside the scope of this book. However, I share the view of many people who consider their use excessive, and welcome moves towards their restriction.

This book is written from my own background of Biochemistry, Medicine and Microbiology, particularly that of food poisoning, and looks at a number of issues at present causing concern. It is not intended to be comprehensive or exhaustive and is not the last word on the subject. Rather it is an attempt to explain the scientific basis of recent worries.

In Part I the consequences of intensive rearing of food animals are considered. The two infections associated with this method—Salmonellosis and Bovine Spongiform Encephalopathy (BSE)—are themselves serious problems, and important warnings, for the system as a whole. Animal welfare and food quality have always been difficult to define. Safety is not, and these issues must cause us to question whether our society is producing meat in an acceptable way.

The effects of antibiotics and the hormone bovine somatotropin (BST) in animal husbandry raise important immediate and long-term issues. The chapter on irradiation hopefully explains that the use of gamma rays is flawed scientifically as a means of controlling much of our food poisoning, and that opposition to their use has a real basis other than through the emotions.

Readers may find the chapter on BSE frightening, particularly because factual information seems to be at variance with what can only be described as government propaganda.

Moving along the food chain in Part II, the food processing industry when it embarked on moist products seemed to be unaware that several dangerous bacteria could grow at refrigerator temperatures. Listeria is well known, but others also exist. The effects of food poisoning are described and, I hope, explained.

Microwave ovens represent another type of food technology that has been largely untested for safety. Perhaps concerns over microwaves represent the theme of this book, also demonstrated by the use of gamma rays, by BSE and by BST: in all these the long-term hazards are not known and are not amenable to experiment in people.

The revolution in convenience foods is central to this debate; it appears at last as if the food industry is beginning to appreciate that solid food cannot be treated in the same way as the centralised production of alcoholic drinks.

Suggestions are given in Chapter 12 and Part III as to how the consumer can avoid problems in the home, and the future role of the supermarket comes under scrutiny. Of course much of our preserved food is safe and can be purchased at infrequent intervals. But should not our perishable food be obtained more frequently from local retailers?

This book may infuriate some farmers, the food industry and some government ministers. I should like to point out that the problems are of their making, not mine. This book suggests some solutions.

University or other departments of 'Food Science' now often working on projects funded by of the food industry will, presumably, be pressured into writing critical reviews. I hope to enjoy reading them. This book is not for the food industry; it is for the intelligent consumer who has the power to improve our food supply by purchasing only what we shall in the future probably call 'real food'. It is hoped that by following my suggestions, the consumer will achieve improvements in the safety and quality of our food.

PART I

*INTENSIVE FARMING METHODS
AND THEIR PROBLEMS*

1 *Intensive Rearing of Food Animals and Poultry*

It must have been around 1953 or 1954, when visiting an aunt and uncle, that I first became aware of intensive rearing of food animals or birds. Sited in their front garden, where there had previously been a vegetable and lawn area, was a huge windowless wooden shed with some strange-looking projections from the roof. 'Broilers' was the then proud explanation. My aunt was a civil servant at the Foreign Office and my uncle a sports reporter; neither had had any worthwhile farming experience. However, the projected profits looked good. The capital to build the shed had been borrowed at low interest, and there were guarantees—or at least near guarantees—from the suppliers of the young chicks, from the feed manufacturers, and from the buyers of the grown chickens. The only staff needed were two inexperienced lads from the village.

There were no problems during the first year, but then a virus struck. The entire flock had to be destroyed. The compensation was inadequate. Debts rose. The venture collapsed.

The reason for describing this incident is that it illustrates many of the important aspects of intensive rearing of food animals (for simplicity poultry will also be described as an 'animal'). In the 1940s, traditional farming methods in the United Kingdom were supplying only about half the country's food requirements. There was obvious pressure to increase efficiency and hence the amount of food produced nationally. The late 1940s and the 1950s saw the development of intensive rearing of poultry for meat (broilers) and for eggs. This was later followed by turkeys, and more recently by ducks. Pigs were also disappearing from the countryside into sheds.

Cows for milk production and mature cattle for beef may also be reared indoors with 'unnatural food' for the winter months, but in general their conditions in the United Kingdom today would not be considered intensive, certainly not in the way that occurs in the United States. Veal, that is cattle reared only to young ages under cramped conditions in sheds, are, however, intensively reared. The rearing of deer for food has come under control, but is still not intensive.

Fish farming of salmon and trout around Western Scotland is a more recent development and is also a type of intensive rearing. It is worth mentioning in passing that the successful farming of salmon and trout must overcome many problems, and the industry is at present only just viable. The problems include infestation of the fish skin by parasites and a general vulnerability to bacterial and fungal infections. The skin parasites are being treated at present with chemicals, traces of which, while probably safe to man in the short term, cannot be accepted in the long term. A solution to the parasite problem is still awaited. That the flesh of so many farmed fish contains antibiotics such as tetracycline is a reflection on the widespread requirement of antibiotics in this type of farming. It is important not to exaggerate the dangers of antibiotics in themselves, but that they are needed so frequently is indicative of the existence of a problem. This issue is considered in Chapter 2.

A further reason for describing my uncle's failed broiler venture is to illustrate that so much of our food farming is motivated primarily, or exclusively, by the desire for profit. This is not to decry such a motive altogether, although adequate safety precautions must always be taken. But if safety is considered subservient to profitability, problems ensue. This is at the heart of the dilemma today.

If an investment is made into intensive rearing facilities such as the building of sheds, with their method of delivery of the feed and water, the systems to constrain the movement of animals, and the means to dispose of the excreta, then the greatest return on capital is achieved by selling as many marketable products in as short a time as possible, before restarting the cycle all over again. The value of food animals is largely determined by their gross weight. Quality is difficult to assess unless, say, pork is thought to be undesirable because it is grossly fatty. Therefore, in running the intensive farm as a purely commercial enterprise, the farmer—or should we say 'investor'—is interested in ways by which the animals can achieve the greatest weight gain over the shortest period for the lowest cost. He will take the minimum precautions needed to control disease, and has been generally unconcerned over the exact composition of the feed, so long as it does its job—of putting on weight. Indeed, he may well be completely unaware of the source of the feed components.

The third aspect of intensive farming that the broiler incident illustrates is that when things go wrong, such as through infections, they can go wrong very badly, and on a major scale. It must be common sense that the closer together animals are reared, the greater the chance of infection passing between each animal or bird. There is a sharp contrast between the way in which many of our food animals are tending to be reared, with that of the human population—at least in the United Kingdom where the majority of people have succeeded in achieving more space. It has been estimated that the average city dweller now commands five times as much indoor air—expressed in terms of cubic yards—as he did a hundred years ago. The greater space has been mainly responsible for reducing the incidence of some diseases such as tuberculosis spread by atmospheric droplets. Antibiotics do have an important role in treating infections in man, but they are less important than factors that prevent the disease.

Intensively reared animals must be more prone to certain diseases than those farmed under conditions of greater space, and it is not surprising that many raw poultry carry bacteria potentially dangerous to man. The problem is aggravated by the conditions at slaughter where such bacteria, perhaps found in a small percentage of live animals, are spread very widely by the procedures used. I am not going to describe these in detail, since you might read no farther! It is hoped, and indeed it is highly probable, that under most conditions the animal is killed humanely. Subsequently, however, most of the procedures that are used have been selected for expediency—that is, the decapitation of, say, poultry, evisceration (removal of guts), and plucking are all performed with a conveyor belt system, with the use of a great deal of water. Those who attempt to justify this system state—correctly—that if each bird was hand-plucked and prepared, the cost to the consumer would rise considerably. I suspect many people would be willing to pay somewhat more for such a product. In the slaughterhouses a similar principle applies for the preparation of red meat from cattle, sheep and pigs—namely that through-put must be sufficiently high for costs to be kept down to the minimum. The standards of hygiene, space and facilities available and the number and depth of inspections are extremely variable, and sometimes inadequate. There is no doubt that the slaughterhouse must increase the risk of the general spread of dangerous microbes from one carcass to others. These will be considered in detail in later chapters.

Let us return to the broiler shed. On the sale of the entire 'crop', the shed is cleaned and made ready for the new chicks. There will be a need to remove the accumulated droppings. These can usually be sold as fertiliser, sometimes after mixing with straw or wood shavings.

Occasionally, horrendous stories break that such manure has been fed to other food animals. This practice is extremely dangerous and hopefully is rare. There is good reason to believe that in 1989 around 200 cattle in Australia died of botulism as a result of this practice. Botulism is an infection that flourishes in organic material where there is no air, as occurs in chickens' droppings. It causes disease in animals and also in man by a toxin or poison that paralyses the muscles, with death resulting from the inability to breathe.

Assuming that the broiler factory will usually dispose of the manure in a sensible way, the main responsibility for the disposal of unwanted components of the food animal rests with the slaughterhouses—in particular, chickens' heads, guts, feet and feathers. With larger animals, the problems are greater, and often include the skin and bones. At present, legislation prevents the retention of this offal at the slaughterhouse other than for very short periods, that is 48 hours. The problem is not new, but is aggravated by intensive farming methods where the rearers of the animals usually have no facilities of their own to dispose of the unwanted remains. On the traditional mixed farm in the past, these items could be dealt with by burial, burning (incineration) or by composting into fertilisers for plants.

Today, these components are treated in rendering plants which are shrouded in secrecy, it being very difficult to gain entry or obtain accurate information concerning their detailed activities. Broadly speaking, rendering plants have developed in line with the needs of intensive farming. The animals' remains are treated with dry or moist heat and converted to two commercially usable products—tallow, a complex fat used for many purposes, including the making of soaps and cosmetics, and a protein-rich fraction to which can be added ground-up bones. This latter product, once finished, is referred to as bone meal and has had a popular use since the 1950s as a garden or agricultural plant fertiliser. It is, of course, the use of this substance as an animal ration that caused Bovine Spongiform Encephalopathy (BSE) or mad cow disease. This will be considered in detail in Chapter 6.

Thus the rendering plants are an integral part of intensive farming, and if, as seems likely, the problems of disposal of the offal are now not capable of economical resolution, then the whole system may collapse.

Rendering plants are not confined to the United Kingdom. They are found in many countries throughout the world, but it is likely that the United Kingdom is the leader in the scale of its rendering industry. The major inherent defect of the system is that the bone meal fraction will be returned to the many animals and birds from which it was derived. It is therefore a type of cannibalism and as such is repulsive to many people. This farming practice was largely hidden from public scrutiny until the salmonella in eggs problem surfaced in November, 1988. Confidence in farming will not return unless it ceases completely.

Information on rendering plants in all countries is difficult to obtain, but there is a suspicion that it was the United Kingdom that initiated the practice of feeding animals with their own products. Presumably the pressures were simply financial—it was cheaper to recycle the animal remains back to animals rather than feed them with vegetable or fish-based supplements, or even use products derived from one species exclusively (e.g. poultry) to feed to another (e.g. pigs). The present system currently does not permit this on any scale, but with some investment, it could be managed. Unfortunately the whole concept of the product 'bone meal' has gained such a bad reputation that it may prove difficult to identify much use for in in the immediate future, other than as a fertiliser.

Problems of Intensively Reared Meat
There are four, sometimes overlapping, problems for meat (and fish) reared by modern methods of intensive

production. These are: first, those of animal welfare; second, quality of the product; third, appeal of the product; and fourth, its safety for the consumer.

Animal Welfare

It must be quite evident that man, by intensive farming methods, is maltreating animals and birds. I shall not dwell on animal welfare matters here, although they will be mentioned subsequently where appropriate. Concern has been expressed by many people in the past, but the effect on the continued operation of the system has until recently been fairly small. However, the combination of welfare worries with the other issues, notably that of safety, has now produced a dramatic revolt against these rearing methods.

Food Quality

This is extremely difficult to define. Taste, smell, texture—such as crispness, toughness, firmness, softness—and the effects of other ingredients that might be added, are all a matter of individual opinion. In particular, whether a taste or smell (these are frequently the same) is good, indifferent, or bad cannot usually be measured scientifically. Yet everyone knows what they like and what they don't. What contributes to the taste and smell of food? Perhaps the most dominant factor is derived from the animal's feed: the colour, taste, smell, and possibly also texture will all be influenced by the diet. For example, poultry fed on fish meal does taste of fish! Personally I don't see anything wrong with this, because I like fish, but other people don't like chicken tasting of fish. Broilers fed with corn go yellow, but do they taste of corn? Fish-farmed salmon tend to be an insipid grey colour unless a pink dye is given to them to replace the effect of their natural pink food.

If we consider the smell and flavours of animals and birds reared in the wild, then many of the important and positive aromas will be derived from vegetable matter, sometimes through eating an intermediate host. Leaves, roots, seeds, berries and flowers are all important. It is not surprising that truly wild birds, such as some ducks, pheasants, partridge, pigeons and woodcock, all have very positive flavours. Indeed, many of us can recall the luxury of real free range chicken or turkey. Today, the image of how the food used to taste lingers on, helped by clever photography and marketing. In reality, the contemporary intensively reared broiler or turkey appears to have very little flavour at all. This is not surprising when there is virtually no natural vegetable material in the feed; rather a considerable proportion of the feed is derived from the rendering plants—the bone meal fraction from its own and other species.

Many people must have become aware of the popularity of poultry products, raw or cooked, with additional herbs, spices or sauces. The need to add real flavour to these food items on such a scale is a sad reflection on the lack of natural taste and smell that they possess after cooking.

It is gratifying to see the recent introduction of free range poultry from retail outlets. Some of these seem to be reared under genuinely free range conditions; others appear to fulfil the definition of 'Pseudo-Free-Range'. This refers to the use of small pens adjacent to large sheds; many birds may not in practice venture outside at all.

Appeal
Interest in food can come from the unexpected. Modern mass production systems create products of uniform size, appearance, texture and taste—what there is of it. Indeed, quality control procedures in industry are specifically required to ensure that the properties of the end product are completely predictable. And for many industrial products, this is not without good reason. It would be folly indeed if, say, a fraction of the gear boxes produced for a particular type of car possessed defects that made them

unreliable or unpredictable. But surely, as far as food is concerned, some variation in taste and smell is something to be desired? Do not our noses and taste buds become dulled by the repetitive eating of exactly the same product?

Safety

Safety issues will be considered in detail in subsequent chapters. There are some people, notably food producers, who think that the risks associated with modern food have been exaggerated. The point is that safety is the only tangible—or definable—parameter of a product that many believe is undesirable on these other grounds: namely, its poor quality, that it is uniformly boring, and that it poses questions of animal welfare.

Our Natural Diet

Before we get too involved in details of what is, and what is not, ideal food, we should ask the fundamental question: 'What should we be eating?' Man, the primate, is biologically an omnivore. The last few thousand years have seen an enormous change in our learning and other intellectual activities, but not much in our physiology, including our digestive system.

Being an omnivore means we are capable of digesting and using both animal and vegetable matter, although not cellulose as ruminants such as cattle and sheep can. Because it is thought that man evolved from lower primates during conditions of relative food shortage, such flexibility in our diet would then have been an advantage for survival against competition. That we are still omnivorous—that is, we still have a broad dietary capability—does not mean that we now have a requirement to eat both meat and vegetables. Nor does it mean that we should necessarily consume one or the other exclusively. This experiment cannot be done, but if we studied the long-term effect of eating only meat or only vegetables, it is the author's guess that the vegetarian diet would be preferable. The main reason for this would be the lack of fibre and polyunsaturated fat in the meat diet.

As far as nutrition is concerned, there are many excellent books suggesting the content of an ideal diet. For example, in broad terms, we know how much protein, total fat, unsaturated fat, carbohydrate, fibre, vitamins and minerals are desirable for different ages and occupations. We also know that the food items which provide these can vary enormously. There is still disagreement over whether some dietary components are essential or generally desirable, in that they will reduce the amounts of some other substances eaten. The point of these comments is that so long as our general diet appears to be adequate in total nutrition, it may not matter exactly what we eat to achieve this. In particular, alternatives to cheap, intensively reared animal food certainly do exist. There is no medical requirement at all to eat meat if we do not choose to.

Energy Conversion

When we eat food, it has a certain energy content or calorific value. The typical adult needs about 1,500-2,000 calories per day. This energy is required to produce heat, replace dying body cells, cause muscles to contract, make the brain function and to provide thousands of other activities essential to life. However, the conversion of chemicals in the food to actual energy in the body is never completely efficient. In the same way a power station, burning coal to produce electricity, produces at best only about half as much electricity as it should, if the potential energy in the coal is calculated mathematically. Most authorities suggest that the overall efficiency of the human body in using energy from food is about 30 per cent. So if we were 100 per cent efficient, instead of 1,500-2,000 calories we would need only 500-660. This inefficiency also applies to other animals. Each species has a characteristic efficiency of conversion of energy from the food, which is almost always less than 50 per cent.

What this means in practice is that the more animal hosts food passes through, the greater is the loss of energy during the process, so that the amount available to the final host—for instance, man— is reduced. For example, if we fed 100g wheat to a growing chicken, it might result in 30g increase in weight. That 30g extra chicken flesh might provide us with 20 calories, whereas if we had eaten the 100g wheat directly, it could have provided 60 calories.

This does not mean that we should all automatically become vegetarian, although it is certainly possible to live completely healthy lives on a purely vegetarian diet. However, some important nutrients can be found in abundance in animal meats, which are present only in small amounts in vegetable matter. It is not my intention to recommend an exclusively vegetarian society. What I want to demonstrate is that modern methods of animal food production fulfil few requirements, whether dietary or gustatory or even those of cost, when it is appreciated how much more efficient vegetarian diets can be. If the issue of safety is added to this debate, then the case must surely become overwhelming to move away from intensive rearing of food animals and towards eating less meat of higher quality derived from animals reared and fed with more respect than under intensive conditions. The protagonists of intensive rearing claim that such movement towards 'organic' or 'free range' or natural would increase the price prohibitively. This is not necessarily so, and any price increase could well be compensated by replacing some of our meat intake with vegetable food.

The best way to feed animals in order for them to put on weight most quickly has been the subject of many experiments. Indeed, the design of modern intensive farms is aimed to achieve such maximum weight gain. Generally, a ready supply of feed, usually dropped by gravity from a high container, or hopper, is provided during the greater part of each day, with lighting adjusted artificially to provide a short period only of rest in each twenty-four hour cycle.

If the animal or bird has to forage for food it expends 'unnecessary' energy (from the point of view of weight gain) in doing so, and misses out on the maximum amount of feed available. Many 'free range' egg-laying chickens are in reality reared intensively in sheds with a door that permits some of them occasionally to venture into a small adjacent pen. Real free range husbandry would seriously interfere with the optimum feeding programme as far as maximum gain of weight is concerned. So it does have to be accepted that, pound for pound, animals reared under free range conditions are somewhat more costly than those cropped by intensive methods.

To achieve the conversion from intensive farming to free range husbandry will be a painful procedure, certainly from the short-term financial view. Help in the form of subsidies may well be required. Ideally, the free range activity will be one component of a mixed farm where waste material from animals or birds can be converted to fertiliser for vegetable crops, notably cereals. This would break the cycle whereby infective agents are currently capable of being returned to the species from which they were derived.

The critical British consumer could find great appeal in locally produced free range red meat, poultry and eggs.

For this change in attitudes towards food production to become really feasible, pressures on the farmer must be released by retailers from providing the cheapest possible products.

TABLE 1

Extent of intensive rearing of food animals and birds

1 Species reared entirely or predominantly under intensive conditions in sheds:

>Chickens (broilers)
>Chickens (egg-layers)
>Turkeys
>Ducks
>Pigs
>Cattle (veal)

2 Species reared partly under intensive conditions:

>Cattle (beef)
>Cows
>Salmon
>Trout

3 Species reared under controlled open spaces:

>Sheep
>Deer
>Pheasants

TABLE 2

Advantages and disadvantages of intensively reared food animals over free range

Advantages

> Greater efficiency of food conversion to meat.
> Predictable yields of meat.
> Ease of husbandry.
> Cheap meat.
> Small space sufficient.

Disadvantages

> Animal welfare concerns.
> Risks of infections and increased incidence of other diseases.
> Requirement for extra drugs.
> Potential death of a greater proportion during rearing.
> Risk of serious epidemics.
> Problems of disposal of excreta.
> Increased risk of drug residues in meat.
> Products without positive taste.
> Products uniform and boring.
> Greater risk of food poisoning to man.

2 *Antibiotics in Intensive Rearing*

Antibiotics are natural chemicals, produced usually by harmless bacteria or fungi, which damage or destroy certain bacteria that can be dangerous. Some antibiotics are used in medicine in the exact form in which they occur in nature, such as in the soil; others are altered from the natural state by small chemical changes to produce improvements, and yet others are now entirely artificial, being synthesised from simple chemicals. During their use over the last fifty years they have become an important, indeed necessary or even central component of human medicine. Their main initial use was in treating infections such as typhoid, tuberculosis and meningitis, which had before not been treatable at all. More recently, they have become an essential part of preventing infections in the ill patient in hospital. However, numerically, antibiotics are most often prescribed for some fairly minor infections in General Practice. The reason for this is that it is still not possible for a doctor, on first seeing a patient, to be sure whether or not a severe infection might be on the point of developing, for which an antibiotic really would be needed. It follows from this that some antibiotics are being prescribed for infections which are not in practice helped by them at all, such as many colds and sore throats.

If the use of antibiotics in human medicine were ideal, then considerable criticism would be justified of their unnecessary use in animals. In this chapter it is proposed that the concerns about the excessive use of antibiotics in animals result not so much from the hazards of the antibiotics in themselves, but from the reasons that require their widespread use.

There are two main types of antibiotic use in animals: either in low doses as a regular addition to the feed, which results in increases in the rate of weight gain, or in short bursts of high doses to control the infections that are, not surprisingly, common under conditions of intensive rearing. The first use, where the drugs are usually referred to as growth promoters, came about by chance, after livestock that had been inadvertently fed the antibiotic tetracycline put on more weight over a certain period than those not fed the antibiotic. This observation has been repeated many times, and it is beyond doubt that the regular feeding of antibiotics to intensively reared animals and birds does cause an increase in the rate of weight gain. It may not be much, perhaps five per cent, but this can be decisive commercially. Thus if a main rearer of, say, pigs or turkeys, puts antibiotics in the feed, and his competitors do not, he is at a considerable advantage. Therefore, in practical terms, if one producer uses antibiotics as growth promoters, then most will. It must be stressed that this increase in weight gain is only likely to occur under conditions of intensive rearing where the penned or caged animals are effectively force-fed.

The cost of the antibiotic is fairly low, so the net effect is to produce a slight lowering of the price. Enthusiasts for such antibiotic use point out that the drugs are merely enabling the maximum rate of weight gain to be achieved. It is interesting that the pharmaceutical companies supplying the antibiotics have been very reluctant to perform experiments, or possibly to publish them, explaining exactly how these drugs achieve their effect of growth promotion. There seems to be an aura of mystery over their action; they are usually sold to the farmer as growth promoters or additives and he may not always appreciate that they are indeed antibiotics.

The most likely explanation for their effect is simply through their antibiotic action. There are some bacteria in the intestines of animals and birds, which produce toxins or poisons that impair—sometimes to a small extent—the well-being of the animal. If these bacteria are removed by antibiotics, then these harmful effects will not occur and the rate of growth can accelerate. The pharmaceutical industry has seemed somewhat reluctant to accept that this is the mode of action of growth-promoting antibiotics; if it did accept this, then the question would immediately be asked, if some bacteria are being removed, which others are taking their place and what effect might this have on human health? To give a specific example, there is indeed some evidence that salmonella carriage in poultry can be encouraged by such antibiotic use.

In the other category of antibiotic use, that is their use for treating actual infections, there is generally greater control of them since a veterinary prescription is usually needed. Intensively reared animals and birds are vulnerable to infections for a number of reasons. The first is that they are bred primarily for their value in food—that is to put on weight as quickly as possible or to produce an uninterrupted supply of eggs. Some elements of their innate resistance to infection might be accidentally lost during breeding and selection. Secondly, the spread of micro-organisms is more likely to occur within sheds than outside, since the main factors destroying microbes in the air—ultraviolet light and drying—may not be effective inside the house. Thirdly, the cramped conditions may reduce the natural vigour and encourage physical assaults between the adjacent penned animals. Fourthly, the cramped space will also permit the ready transfer by touch of microbes between the animals or birds.

A number of methods are available to control infections in intensive rearing, other than the use of antibiotics. When vulnerability to a particular infection is recognised, a vaccine can be developed and given either in the feed or by injection. When the first signs of an infection occur, an individual animal or just a few can be destroyed before further spread. Sometimes, every animal or bird within the farm or batch may have to be destroyed. Reasons for this include well-known infections such as 'foot and mouth' disease, 'swine fever', or 'fowlpest'. It is interesting that, with each of these, the prime motivation for slaughter is to prevent spread and damage to animals at further farms, rather than to prevent any risk to man.

Antibiotics do have an important role in preventing and treating infections in intensively reared animals, and to a lesser extent in animals reared 'naturally'. Indeed, without antibiotics, and also the related drugs active against fungi, it is likely that intensive rearing would not be viable. There is enormous commercial pressure from the pharmaceutical industry, from farmers and from some veterinarians, to ensure adequate availability of antibiotics in food production.

So what are the snags? It must be admitted that several of these are still unproven, and it is possible that of all aspects of intensive rearing, the use of antibiotics has received most unjust publicity. Some of the worries emanate from the nature of the antibiotic, in that similar compounds are used in both veterinary and human medicine (veterinary medicine, incidentally, includes the husbandry of food animals). First, the consumer might unwittingly drink or eat the antibiotic, with possible ill effects; secondly, the use of antibiotics in animals might cause the appearance of bacteria resistant to them, and these might spread to the human population and prevent our antibiotics from being effective. Thirdly, there could be problems not with the whole resistant bacteria, but from the tiny pieces of nucleic acid (DNA) that are responsible for the resistance; these fragments of DNA could enter human bacteria.

Antibiotic Residues
After an animal or bird has stopped receiving an antibiotic, either as a growth promoter or to treat an infection, the

drug will be expelled from its body over the following few days or weeks. Companies marketing antibiotics have to show how quickly this occurs, and their research is checked by both civil servants and independent scientists. As many drugs are expelled either through the kidney and urine, such as penicillin, or through the liver, such as the antibiotic erythromycin, it is the falling concentrations in these organs that are most closely followed after the antibiotic has ceased to be administered. Let us suppose that no antibiotic (or other drug) can be detected in a few animals' carcasses after one day of stopping treatment, then, because of the need to anticipate some variation in the rates of expulsion between animals, a cautious withholding time of five days might be identified. Such a withholding time means, first, that it is believed that after five days from the end of use of that antibiotic, we are confident that no traces of the drug will remain in any tissues that might provide potential food; and secondly, the farmer, his veterinary adviser and all those involved in the first stages of the food chain must comply with this stipulation. Moreover, this becomes a necessary requirement for the use of that antibiotic in the first place. That means it can only be used, either as a feed additive or as veterinary prescription, with the strict requirement that an interval of five days must elapse between the completion of the treatment and the slaughter and possible consumption of animal parts.

All drugs administered to food animals should have precise instructions over their control—that is the withdrawal period. A great deal of money, effort and debate goes into identifying what these periods should be. Moreover, as our methods of measuring traces of drugs improve, so we can be even more certain that no drug whatsoever will be present in the food we eat. So, what is the problem? Very simply, it is human nature and the reality of farming and the meat trade, so that there is almost a near-impossibility of ensuring that such withholding times are adhered to. The difficulty of mounting a prosecution against those in breach of the rules is also considerable.

First consider the farmer. Can he really appreciate all the different withholding times of all the different drugs he may use? Market forces determine the exact day when animals or poultry are required and are slaughtered. Will not many farmers be tempted into receiving a good slaughter price for an animal, even if the withholding period is incomplete? How does the farmer know when to change the feed containing an antibiotic to one that does not? He cannot always anticipate the need five days forward. Or consider another example—the sick animal treated quite legitimately with antibiotics. Suppose that the veterinarian and the farmer agree that slaughter is the only answer, and that the animal that is being treated is not suitable for human food. As such, its value is only a fraction of the price of an untreated healthy carcass. However, there is a substantial trade in slaughtered animals among unscrupulous dealers, and there is very little to prevent one dealer from selling the diseased and treated carcass as if it were for human consumption.

Let us hope this practice is rare, but these examples do illustrate that, however demanding the theoretical controls of antibiotics may be, there are extreme difficulties in enforcing them.

The next question to consider is whether eating small amounts of antibiotic in our food is dangerous. The first reassuring point is that many antibiotics used in human medicine are identical to those in veterinary use. Those in human use have a very vigorous safety assessment, and because by and large antibiotics act on the parts of the bacterium that have no human equivalent, they are relatively safe as drugs go. We must next remember that these same drugs may also be used unnecessarily in animals—for example, for treating virus infections for which they have no role. Next we should be aware that some of our own indigenous or harmless bacteria and fungi (referred to as commensals) can produce antibiotics in us. The micro-organisms that cause athlete's foot can produce penicillin! Finally, the published evidence relating side-effects from antibiotics to their presence in food is small. This is not surprising, since once food has been eaten, it is not usually available for testing at a later date! However, one important example was the occurrence of illness after drinking milk containing penicillin. This occurred in a single individual who drank milk contaminated with penicillin and then developed a skin rash.

To conclude, we can state that whilst the theoretical constraints preventing us from eating meat or drinking milk containing antibiotics are meticulous, they are not capable of being enforced in practice. However, the evidence incriminating ingestion of antibiotics as a direct major threat to human health is flimsy, at least at present. But let this not detract from our goal of zero antibiotic consumption from food, and of reducing such use to a minimum in farming.

Antibiotic Resistance

Most people are aware that if bacteria become resistant to an antibiotic then that drug will not work in a serious infection and the results could be catastrophic. The reason for this is that the most important aspect of the role of antibiotics in life-threatening infections is their immediate use. This urgency is needed to kill the bacteria before they have time to produce poisons or toxins that might damage the patient. Therefore, in a serious infection, doctors must be confident that the drug they have selected will work reliably. It is not satisfactory to take the attitude that if the first drug fails, then a subsequent choice may work; it may well be too late.

A good example is the treatment of meningitis. During the 1950s–70s antibiotics reduced the risk of dying from bacterial meningitis from nearly 100 per cent to about ten per cent. The risk of death is still about ten per cent because in the last few years we have been unable to treat the disease any more quickly than we used to. It is therefore essential—when considering the human use of antibiotics—that we do all we can to prevent the effectiveness of those antibiotics required for the treatment of life-threatening infections from being jeopardised through the appearance of antibiotic resistance. It is this worry that questions much of the veterinary use of antibiotics. But first, we must try and understand antibiotic resistance.

In nature some micro-organisms, such as fungi and bacteria, have presumably 'learnt' by chance that if they make and release chemicals deterring other microbes, they will keep more food and space to themselves. The problem comes if those chemicals or antibiotics released also damage the micro-organisms producing them. So, for the producer microbe to benefit from the release of its destructive chemical, it has to be resistant to that substance. Antibiotic resistance therefore arose in association with antibiotic production in the first place. The two were initially inseparable, but over millions of years, some bacteria or fungi evolved or changed so that they either only produced the antibiotic, or else had the ability to resist it. It is increasingly coming as less of a surprise when we document high incidences of antibiotic resistance after intensive antibiotic use.

Let us consider the primitive bacterial cell, producing two particular products—one the antibiotic, and the other a substance found, say, on its surface and capable of neutralising the harmful effects of that chemical. These substances might well be penicillin (the antibiotic) and penicillinase (correctly called β-lactamase) which prevents the penicillin from destroying the cell that makes it.

We now appreciate that all such substances produced by a cell have a length of DNA responsible for creating them.

We also know that DNA is changing all the time, sometimes becoming structured into small circles that can pass between different bacteria. In due course, the production of penicillin and penicillinase became separated, so that by the early part of this century, penicillin was found to be produced by some microbes and a few others were resistant to it. What man has done, by artificial means, is to amplify dramatically the amount of penicillin in our environment as a whole. The net result is that the numbers of bacteria that could produce penicillinase have increased.

Against this background, the use of antibiotics in food production might jeopardise antibiotic use in man in two ways. First, antibiotic-resistant bacteria themselves may pose a threat. As with residues, there are two views. We can argue that antibiotic use in food animals must select for resistant bacteria, and the longer the drugs are used, the greater that trend. We can also argue that many human diseases requiring antibiotics can be caused by bacteria found in food animals. It can be stressed that such resistant bacteria selected in animals can spread to man through meat itself, abattoir working, farmers, butchers, veterinary and other intermediary vectors, such as insects, pets or birds. Infections from animals, which cause problems in man, are referred to as zoonoses. Therefore it is argued that zoonoses as a whole may fail to respond to antibiotics as a result of antibiotic use in animals.

The opposite view is equally emphatic. First, it does not deny that antibiotics in food animals select resistance in those bacteria in those animals. Moreover, it suggests that some of these resistant bacteria may not be as viable—that is able to persist in the long term—as those which are antibiotic-sensitive. There is indeed experimental evidence in support of this. There are few micro-organisms which have learnt to resist antibiotics, and which also possess an enhanced capacity to damage their host, be it human or animal. Most antibiotic-resistant bacteria have a capability to cause disease similar to those which are antibiotic-sensitive, or, on occasion, a reduced capability. Then there is the observation that most zoonoses either do not require antibiotics for treatment (these include food poisoning due to salmonella or campylobacter) or, if antibiotics are needed, resistance may be less of a problem, as with listeriosis, animal staphylococci, brucellosis, or streptococcal disease. This is probably true overall. Then, it is apparent that most 'animal' bacteria survive rather poorly in 'human' environments. The argument continues that antibiotic use in animals would only be of major importance to humans if there was not such a degree of unnecessary antibiotic use in humans in the first place. This latter point cannot be refuted. When looking for actual evidence from patients where antibiotic use in animals has been responsible for important treatment failures, we are left only with the exceptional case of food poisoning salmonella that is resistant to antibiotics, and which also invades the body rather than being confined to the gut. This may fail to respond to treatment in the elderly or in children. But these instances seem few indeed. However, the counter-argument again is that whilst these occasions are only rarely identified, their occurrence may actually be more common.

Can Resistance Genes Spread From Animal Bacteria to Human?

Again the arguments are balanced. It has been indicated that resistance to antibiotics can be caused (or determined or coded—the correct scientific terms) by small pieces of circular DNA known as R-factors, which are capable of transfer between bacteria. Among such possible cases of transfer is the movement from an animal to a human bacterium, so that as a result of use of antibiotics in animals the latter gains hereditary material which endows resistance. This is certainly true in theory, and perhaps occurs occasionally in practice.

The counter-arguments are equally significant. First, most R-factors in human bacteria are selected (that is, their presence is encouraged) by the use, often unnecessary, of antibiotics in man. Secondly, if such R-factors did spread from animal bacteria to human, they would not be expected to survive very long, since each R-factor is most suited to survival in one particular type of bacterium. This might mean that R-factors found naturally in animal bacteria are much better suited to persist in those bacteria, rather than in the human. Thirdly, it could be argued that antibiotic use in man could select human R-factors capable of transferring to animal strains.

Despite these uncertainties over the real importance of R-factors, a government committee under Lord Swann reported in 1969 that there was some real concern over antibiotic use in animals as a threat to the treatment of human infections. It suggested that antibiotics such as penicillin or tetracycline, used for treating human infections, should not be used as growth promoters in food animals, although they could be used as treatment for animal infections. This would seem to be a characteristic compromise in the light of uncertain scientific evidence. Nevertheless, this advice has been heeded by and large, although there is no way of judging its impact on resistance in bacteria of either human or animal origin.

To summarise, antibiotics in food animals may pose a risk to man; certainly they confer no benefit. Perhaps the most worrying aspect of the continuing debate over the extent of potential harm is that we have forgotten the reason for their use—either as growth promoter for purely commercial reasons, or for treating infections, frequently generated by the conditions of intensive rearing. Antibiotics are best seen in the general context, not themselves being especially dangerous, but the extent of their use being a reflection of the intrinsically unsatisfactory nature of intensive rearing of food animals.

TABLE 3

Impact of antibiotics on intensive rearing

Advantages

Increase slightly the rate of conversion of feed to gross weight.

Treating and preventing the increased risk of infections.

Profit for manufacturers, retailers and veterinary surgeons.

Disadvantages

May be present in meat at time of slaughter.

May cause side-effects in the animal.

Can alter bacteria in the animal, for example towards greater salmonella carriage.

Will select resistant bacteria in the treated animals.

Resistant bacteria may spread to man.

Some component genes of the resistant bacteria may become established in human bacteria.

Cost.

TABLE 4

Possible reasons for antibiotic residues in meat

Farmer does not plan to change to antibiotic-free feed before slaughter.

Demand for meat products occurs unpredictably.

Treatment of the animal with the wrong dose of antibiotic.

Treated infected animals getting into the food chain through accident or unscrupulous dealers.

Withholding periods often calculated from pharmaceutical company's own data and may not be long enough.

Unawareness by the farmer that certain feeds may contain antibiotics.

Failure of communication along food chain from farm to slaughterhouse.

3 *Bovine Somatotropin (BST)*

Bovine Somatotropin or BST is the hormone in cows that is responsible for milk production. Hormones are chemical messengers produced in one part of the animal's (or human's) body that act on another. Under natural conditions, giving birth to the calf stimulates the production of BST which in turn increases milk production in the udder. Similar hormones exist in other mammals, including humans. One particular substance in humans that has some degree of resemblance to BST is known as growth hormone, whose chief function is exactly as the name suggests, being responsible for growth in children. Other hormones which have some similarities in their chemical structure affect the thyroid, fertility, the onset of labour, digestion and sugar use. It may not be just the entire chemical that can produce these effects: small or even large pieces (known as fragments) can be active. Moreover, some whole hormones, or their fragments, that have effects against one so-called target gland or organ may have other activities and these may not always have been identified.

That BST promotes the production of cow's milk has been known for most of this century, with much of the early work performed in the Soviet Union. Because of the similarities between BST and human growth hormone, and the extreme difficulty in obtaining a supply of human growth hormone in the 1940s and 1950s, tests were done to see if injections of BST from cows could help those children with a deficiency of human growth hormone. No effect was seen—the children did not grow. This is the only experimental evidence there is concerning the possible safety of artificial BST in people. We shall return to this later.

During the last forty years, cows have been bred progressively to yield more milk through painstaking identification of those with the greatest milk yield and breeding only from them. One of the problems with the cow's udder is that if it is overfilled with milk, there is a greater risk of an infection known as mastitis. This has serious consequences for the cow, and possibly the farmer, since the milk might dry up prematurely. Treatment of mastitis can succeed with antibiotics, but unless rigorous precautions are taken, there is a risk of both harmful bacteria and antibiotics getting into the milk. However, some cases of mastitis are difficult to treat.

Because the milk yield from cows is now so high, it is certainly arguable whether attempts to increase it further have any value. Nevertheless, it has been obvious for some time that if the amount of BST in the milk-producing, or lactating, cow could be increased, then the amount of milk would increase. When those ideas were first suggested, the amount of milk produced from any one cow was much less than it is now, and such ideas then—say ten to twenty years ago—may not have been so unreasonable as they seem now.

One point about milk production that should be stressed is the very wide variation in its composition and in its amount. Factors responsible for this include the nature of the herds, the type of grassland, the composition of artificial feeds, the stage in time of lactation, and the farming husbandry, such as the hygiene of the herd and the frequency and type of milking. It is very difficult to specify exactly what is normal milk, particularly since it has been undergoing change over the last few decades.

To return to the plan to increase BST in cows, the only way of achieving this would appear to be to put more of the hormone into the cow by injection, since it apparently would not get into the body after being eaten. In the early years, the real problem was to find and purify enough natural BST from cows at the end of their lives to inject into others. This problem arose because the organ that makes BST in the cow is very small. Precisely the same problem was being met with the attempts to extract enough human growth hormone from people after death to inject into children who had a deficiency of it. Incidentally, on some occasions the infectious agent for Creutzfeldt-Jakob disease (see Chapter 6) was accidentally transferred by this procedure, with fatal consequences.

Up to about 1972, there was no practical prospect of obtaining an adequate supply of extra BST to inject into cows. But 1972 really saw the birth of genetic engineering. Over twenty years before, Watson and Crick had established the structure of DNA, a single large twisted molecule. This substance is responsible for the 'memory' of the cell that drives it to produce proteins, including substances such as BST and human growth hormone. But the DNA molecule is one enormous chemical and difficult to break up into usable pieces. It was work in the USA around 1972 that identified a series of enzymes which could not only break up DNA into small pieces at exactly known sites, but could subsequently join them together again in a different order. Immediately, the potential of this technique was apparent. For BST, the procedure could go as follows: take from the cow a few cells that make the hormone, then break the DNA from these into small pieces using the enzymes (which are known, incidentally, as restriction endonucleases). At the same time take a small piece of DNA from a bacterium (this piece is usually an R-factor, see Chapter 2), break this also into small pieces, then stew the two different sets of fragments together under conditions that favour the rejoining of the pieces. Sooner or later a fragment of DNA from the cow, with the memory to make any cell produce BST, becomes part of the bacterial R-factor. It is then easy to put these hybrid

DNA elements back into the bacterium, known as *E. coli.* Bacteria such as *E. coli* grow at a phenomenal rate. One bacterial cell can multiply into more than a million in eight hours, whereas it is exceedingly difficult to make any mammalian cells grow at all in the laboratory, let alone quickly. What is more, if conditions are made exactly right, the memory of the cow DNA tricks the bacterium into making BST. The net result would appear to be an endless supply of cheap BST.

An American company did indeed perform these experiments in 1977–9. When the full potential of genetic engineering was first appreciated, some of the initial excitement was dampened by calls for safety controls to prevent the escape of newly created life forms. Now all such experiments are carefully controlled, but almost any piece of DNA can seemingly be so manipulated. It follows from this that genetic engineering can generate two types of product. Either it can create an abundant supply of proteins valuable to mankind or it can produce a supply of substances of no value or even of detriment. There is nothing that seems to be inherently good or bad about the technique itself (although some people will argue otherwise on moral grounds). What matters is the nature of the final product and, most importantly, how it is used.

Indeed two benefits attributable to genetic engineering must immediately be acknowledged. Human growth hormone is now made by this technique, and has the advantage over that obtained from human material in that the genetically engineered product will not carry the risk of transmitting Creutzfeldt-Jakob disease.

Perhaps of more significance is the production of human insulin by genetic engineering. This has been pioneered by the American pharmaceutical company, Eli Lilly. Most diabetics requiring insulin have, until the last few years, received the hormone from pig or cow sources. In the 1980s, the demand was beginning to look as if it would outstrip supply within a few years; genetic engineering has prevented this occurring. Whilst there have been some difficulties in finding the best way of using human insulin in treating diabetics, its availability must be greeted with enthusiasm. In three words, we need it.

In the following pages, I am going to take a particularly tough line with artificial BST, because neither we, the consumers, nor the cow need it. Since artificial BST is slightly different from the natural hormone, the artificial or synthetic product will be referred to as s-BST.

Structure of s-BST

There is some slight variation in the detailed chemical structures of natural BST obtained from different animals. Each chemical is made up of a long chain of amino acids, the building blocks which, when joined together, constitute the final protein. However, s-BST differs from the natural hormone in that one of the end (or terminal) amino acids is methionine, an unusual substance in that place and not present there in the natural hormone. Why s-BST contains this end methionine is not clear, at least not to me. It might result from the problems of the junction of the cows' DNA with that of the bacterial, required to make the whole DNA operate, or it could be involved in the extraction and stability of the artificial hormone.

By the early 1980s, a number of American pharmaceutical companies had acquired permission (very costly) from the company holding the patents, Genentech, to research s-BST in the hope that the drug could increase the yield of milk in many countries.

By the middle 1980s two companies had applied to the Ministry of Agriculture, Fisheries and Food (MAFF), and had been granted permission to do trials in this country. The document authorising this permission was described as an animal trials certificate (ATC), and was considered by the chief scientific advisory committee to MAFF, the Veterinary Products Committee (VPC). I was a member of that committee but had no involvement in the decision. At the time, the companies had claimed that the milk from cows treated with s-BST was similar to that from untreated cows, so it was felt reasonable to add this milk to the general pool while thorough experiments were being undertaken. With any food that has the potential to cause problems in the long term, the risks from a brief exposure of a much diluted product (as would occur in the pool) must be quite different from those that might result from the exclusive consumption over many years of what is, in effect, a new food. The debate about whether this should have been permitted, rather than the milk being discarded, is very much less important than the question of what the effect might be in the future on a community required to consume only s-BST stimulated milk and other dairy products.

By 1988 the pharmaceutical companies had generated substantial amounts of research data and were requesting the VPC to recommend the granting of a product licence. By 1990, the two intervening years had seen a series of leaked claims to the press, suggesting the existence of safety worries, countered by claims by the companies and indeed by government ministers, usually to the effect that s-BST was completely safe, certainly for human use. In this chapter both the companies' and the opposing views will be presented, regrettably sometimes vaguely because of the oppressive legislation governing secrecy. While the new 1989 Official Secrets Act excludes most areas of commercial activity, the existing 1968 Medicines Act certainly does not.

There are six types of problem that s-BST raises. One may generate another—for example, if s-BST does cause mastitis to increase in the cow, this could increase the consumer's chances of drinking infected milk and suffering harmful effects. The six worries are:

1 Dangers to humans over the long term.
2 Immediate dangers to the cow, long-term dangers to the cow and indeed to the whole cattle-breeding industry.

3 Animal welfare concerns.
4 Environmental and economical issues.
5 The defects in the 1968 Medicines Act regarding the necessity for a particular drug.
6 The question of the need for research independent of that undertaken by the pharmaceutical companies concerned.

Long-term Dangers to Humans

Apart from mastitis (see p. 54), there is unlikely to be any short-term ill effect on human health from s-BST milk. In the same way, if there really is proof that excessive butter is bad for health, it is the repetitive eating of the animal fat over the years that will generate risk; one is not likely to develop a heart attack after a single fatty meal! The possibility of adverse effects on human health results from the expected scale of consumption of s-BST milk. Because the volume of milk produced by a cow treated with s-BST typically increases by about one-sixth or a seventh (i.e. 15 per cent), those farmers using the chemical would, presumably, be able to charge rather less than those not using it, and the latter would soon become pressurised into using it too. Then, after an interval during which the number of cows would be reduced by around 15 per cent, the actual prices for milk might well harden once more. The Milk Marketing Board, and the dairy industry as a whole, would find great difficulties in generating two pools of milk, one natural and the other stimulated by s-BST. It would not be possible for the consumer to order the preferred type for general doorstep delivery. Perhaps a few specialist outlets might be able to stock 'natural' milk if s-BST milk became standard, in the same way that unpasteurised milk is still available. This situation would be quite different from irradiated food which should be easy to avoid in retail outlets, if not in restaurants.

Perhaps, at this point, the view of the companies and those others supporting the availability of s-BST milk should be stated. These protagonists seem to include MAFF officials, and some larger producers who see s-BST as a device to remove competition from smaller farmers. These point out there is no proven long-term safety problem for man, that the chemical composition of milk is in any case variable and that s-BST milk contains constituents at concentrations within the normal range. Moreover, milk yield, and hence the amount of natural BST and other chemicals it stimulates, have been increasing anyway over the last decade, and no untoward effects have been detected.

But the effects of changes in milk composition may take decades to manifest themselves, and even longer to analyse. With s-BST milk, the fatty acids that are the major components of the globules of milk fat appear to be somewhat different from those in normal milk: the s-BST fatty acids seem to possess greater chain length than usual. Another change is that s-BST stimulates the synthesis of substances that have some type of insulin effect. These are known as insulin-like growth factors (e.g. IGF-1). It is not known what the longer-term effects of these changes are. We can speculate, hope, or just wait and see. The problem is that experiments cannot be done to find out what such effects might be. Both the practicality and the ethics on any study in humans are daunting, to say the least. What is more, if s-BST were made generally available, it would be very difficult to identify the control group in any planned experiment; these would be the people not consuming any s-BST milk or dairy products, who would otherwise be matched well for characteristics with the group to be treated.

The effect of s-BST itself on human health poses another worry. The manufacturers state that the synthetic hormone resembles the natural one, being about 98–99 per cent similar, that it should be thought of as being exactly equivalent to the natural hormone. This may or may not be a valid interpretation; the rogue methionine in s-BST could generate some problems. Furthermore, because of the tendency for DNA to change spontaneously (what is now referred to as mutation), the bacteria, or at least some of them making s-BST, could alter and produce some further changes in the s-BST chemical which might then go undetected by the usual routine checks. It has been pointed out that natural BST, given by injection in experiments performed many years ago, was not found to have any effect on children—at least as far as can be told. This does not automatically guarantee that s-BST cannot produce any effect. In theory, the following events could all happen. First, it is possible that s-BST might to some extent be absorbed from the mouth or intestines; if it were, then it could produce some adverse action on the body's metabolism. It is more likely, however, that enzymes from our intestines would break the intact hormone into small pieces. If these were then absorbed, effects on growth could be seen. The reason for considering this possibility is that, whilst the whole natural hormone appears not to have any action, fragments of it do seem to, in that they increase the amount of nitrogen held by the body. This means that one or more pieces of the broken-up natural hormone would be likely to affect growth, if it were absorbed from the intestines or mouth. It is relevant that the average height in Western civilisation has increased over the last century. It is possible that some of this increase has resulted from the eating and absorption of natural BST in milk. Put another way, we may at the moment already be consuming more bovine somatotropin than is good for us!

The possibility that biologically active fragments from s-BST might be formed in our intestines, and then absorbed, must be taken seriously, but seems completely impossible to investigate experimentally.

So far, the potential long-term ill effects on human health from s-BST itself and other products stimulated by it have been looked at theoretically. If any effects were observed in practice, what might the actual effects be on human health? Since these chemicals mainly affect fat, sugars, and growth, it follows that coronary heart disease and strokes, the development of diabetes, and disturbances of bones could occur at greater frequencies than usual. The companies argue that this is wild speculation and that there is no evidence for any of these effects. Of course, there is not, and cannot be, as has been explained already. It is not up to us, the consumers, to prove the product is dangerous. It is the responsibility of the makers of s-BST to show it is safe in people. If such experiments cannot be done, this is their problem, not ours.

Another possible effect from absorption of the entire s-BST hormone, or from its fragment containing the end methionine group, could be stimulation of antibodies to it. There is a tendency for this to occur with other genetically-engineered hormones, and indeed in some cows treated with s-BST. The effect of the antibody is to neutralise some of the activity of s-BST, and possibly also the natural BST. Antibodies are produced in the cow presumably because the animal's immune system recognises s-BST as foreign. There seems no reason to doubt that some humans would react similarly, assuming that the s-BST would be absorbed, at least partly, from the mouth or intestines. If this happened, these antibodies might interact not only with our natural growth hormone but with other hormones.

Readers will now be familiar with some of the problems of intensive rearing of food animals. These fall into two categories: aspects of the system may be inherently dangerous, or the theoretically ideal controls may not in practice be applied. With mastitis, and its possible harm to human health, both these issues could apply. If a cow develops an infection of the udder, the early or later stages of the infection may go unnoticed, with resultant bacteria contaminating the milk. Monitoring of milk safety is done primarily by counting cells, rather than bacteria, in the milk, so the latter could be missed. Moreover, not all milk is sold through the Milk Marketing Board, with its regular surveillance procedures. It could be argued that pasteurisation of milk should be capable of eliminating any undesirable bacteria, but not all milk is pasteurised, and in early 1989 the Minister of Agriculture specifically guaranteed that the consumer would continue to have the opportunity of purchasing unpasteurised milk, if he or she so wished.

Once a cow is known to be suffering from mastitis, then it is usually treated by injecting high concentrations of antibiotic into the affected regions of the udder. Theoretically the milk should not enter the milk pool until some days after the completion of treatment. However, in practice we may not always be able to rely on this; there could therefore be an increased risk of swallowing antibiotics (see Chapter 2).

Several of the bacteria that cause mastitis in cows can have deleterious effects on man, and are capable of causing diarrhoea, food poisoning, arthritis, and blood poisoning. The bacteria include salmonella, *Staphylococcus aureus*, *Listeria monocytogenes*, campylobacter, and streptococci.

Dangers to the Cow
The regular injection of s-BST has some pronounced effects on the body chemistry, or metabolism. By diverting the general use of nutrients to the udder, there must be a risk of side-effects. The following are the concerns: reduced fertility, distorted structure of bones, the causing of diabetes, anaemia, reduced immunity against infection and possible weakness of muscles. Mastitis would be expected to result from an increased volume of milk entering the udder. The extent to which these adverse effects occur in practice must depend on how the cows are reared. The companies claim that these side-effects either do not occur or, if they do, they are not more prevalent

than in any cow yielding high volumes of milk.

For the full effect of s-BST on increased milk production to be realised, the cow must receive ample feed at all times. If adequate feed were not always available, these mooted side-effects could become troublesome because s-BST would in effect divert nutrients from the various functions in the cow to that producing more milk. For example, if insufficient nutrients were available for both production of red blood cells and increased amounts of milk, the end result could be increased milk and a shortage of red cells—that is, anaemia.

Under the trials that have been performed, great care has been taken by the manufacturers of the drug to ensure adequate supplies of feed at all times. In practice this can mean intensive rearing. Under such conditions, it is possible that the use of s-BST is not associated with many immediate side-effects. However, were s-BST to be used 'routinely' there would appear to be a likelihood of unwanted consequences. Either the cows would be reared intensively, with all the problems implicit in that system, or free-ranging cows could well suffer side-effects as a result of the failure to control feed intake adequately. The crucial question arising from so much experimental data on food animals is, how relevant to the real world are experiments performed under ideal conditions?

BSE will be discussed in detail in Chapter 6. Many cows are likely to be infected with the agent, but appear to be well. This occurs because the infectious agent is thought to begin to multiply and spread months or even years before the illness occurs.

It is known that many hormones or drugs can aggravate infections by reducing the capacity of the host to tolerate the micro-organism. It is therefore possible that s-BST could aggravate BSE, in that it could cause the illness to develop sooner or in more animals. Of more concern would be the possibility that by reducing any natural host resistance to it, s-BST could increase the shedding of the

BSE agent from the tissues into, say, the gut, and hence onto the ground.

The counter-argument is that there is no evidence for this. Again this is true, but no research has been performed. In any case, such research would be very difficult with the present knowledge because it is not possible to identify cows infected with the BSE agent, which are not yet showing signs of illness.

Animal Welfare

In addition to the animal welfare issues generated by the need for control over the feed, the use of s-BST raises the question of the morality of the regular injection of a drug that is conferring no benefit to the animal. It is likely that the injection would be made at two-weekly intervals into one of the animal's quarters. Some pain and swelling are inevitable following each injection, but how can these be assessed for tolerability from the animal's point of view? It is difficult even to consider how procedures might be established to attempt to answer these questions.

The companies claim that their veterinary trialists—the people who are actually responsible for administering the drug—state that the animals soon become tolerant of the injection. It would be necessary to see an independent analysis of this claim before it were accepted.

Environmental and Economical Issues

The environmental issues are, perhaps, more straight-forward. Assuming that s-BST were generally used and milk production increased by 15 per cent and our consumption of dairy products remained constant, then around 15 per cent fewer cows would be needed. The process of reducing dairy herds by this amount would certainly cause difficulties for some farmers. Those most vulnerable to commercial pressures would be the keepers of small herds and those determined not to use s-BST. Assuming that reduction in numbers would be realistically achievable, is this a desirable goal? Indeed, is greater efficiency of food production intrinsically desirable? The manufacturers claim that if s-BST were used to increase milk production from the same number of cows, the increased supply of milk would help alleviate the world's shortage. But is there not already a tendency to overproduce milk in Western Europe? Are there not maximum quotas that dairy farmers may not exceed, to keep the volume of milk down to manageable amounts? Surely, the real problem of food shortages involves the distribution from overproducing to underproducing nations. Of course, not all improvements in efficiency in food production are undesirable, but it is essential to ensure that, globally, distribution networks are satisfactory. It is also essential that if the volume of food production to a malnourished community is increased, the population does not simply increase at a rate commensurate with that of its food. To convert a small malnourished to a large malnourished community is hardly progress!

Defects in Drug Legislation

Synthetic BST raises some awkward questions concerning the legislation of drugs in the United Kingdom and elsewhere. Any pharmaceutical company wishing to obtain permission to market a product has to comply with detailed laws contained in the 1968 Medicines Act. The three aspects of this Act that must be satisfied are those of quality, efficacy and safety. Quality defines matters such as purity and stability—that is, the absence of decomposition of the product during its shelf-life. Efficacy identifies whether the product produces the medicinal effect as claimed, and safety speaks for itself. The question of efficacy also applies to particular effects the drug may have on chemical changes in the animal or man, regardless of whether or not any benefit is conferred. That s-BST affects some of the chemical interactions in the cow means that it has been assessed under the 1968 Medicines Act.

The real problem is that there are no clauses within this Act that require any product to be beneficial, or indeed to be needed at all. Surely a requirement of need should be the first and most important clause in any Medicines Act. That is, if a drug substance is not needed, or rather if the companies intent on marketing it have not established a need, it should not be considered further. There is an urgent need to amend this Act to include this provision.

Independent Research
The last worry with s-BST has been the little amount of trial work performed by workers other than employees of the companies involved with its development. This does not, of course, imply any criticism of the integrity of the companies concerned. It is, however, only human nature for the manufacturer of a product to plan studies likely to show their product in its best possible light. There is a real need for s-BST to be assessed under actual farming conditions, and for the trials and results to be monitored by truly independent observers. Unfortunately, the loss of funding of independent research in the United Kingdom will make this extremely difficult in the future.

To sum up, the availability of s-BST reflects many of the problems inherent in new technology for which there is not a pressing need. Unless great care is taken with the use of this type of product, the long-term adverse effects could require very tough and costly action in the future. Before any technology that increases the complexity of the food chain is introduced, it surely must be required to provide undisputed benefits; otherwise, as might occur here, the effects could be undesirable, both for the cow and for the consumer.

TABLE 5

Bovine Somatotropin (s-BST)—the issues

Advantages

Increased milk yield—by around 15 per cent.

Disadvantages

Change of composition of milk presents uncertain danger to man.

Impossible to research effect on man.

If licensed, most consumers would be forced to consume s-BST milk.

Long-term and short-term side-effects in cow probable.

Pain and swelling in the cow at the site of injection.

Disadvantages small dairy herds.

No certainty of long-term reduction in milk price.

Shows up weakness in 1968 Medicines Act that may pave way for other unnecessary drugs.

4 Chickens and Eggs

Intensive rearing of food animals and birds is seen at its most extreme with poultry. Chickens and eggs are the commonest source of food poisoning, notably that due to salmonella and campylobacters. Moreover, the feed frequently contains material from the rendering plants, and the quality, as far as taste, smell and interest of most broilers are concerned, is abysmal.

Egg production and the 'cultivation' of chicken meat use different breeds of chicken. Whilst broilers can lay eggs if they reach sufficient maturity, the eggs are pretty small and are produced unreliably. The meat of the discarded egg-layer is of limited value, being suitable only for use as pet food or in some processed items such as soups, pies and fillers. The master breeding flocks for broilers are based both in the United Kingdom and in Europe. The egg-layers are derived from master or elite flocks in Holland and France, which supply many European countries.

The contamination of broilers with food poisoning bacteria presents a more straightforward problem than the egg-layers. Salmonella is found naturally in a small proportion of broiler chickens, where it may or may not cause disease. Campylobacter is found in most and rarely causes illness. When present, both these types of bacteria will be predominantly in the intestines. Regardless of whether the bacteria are initially in a few or in many birds, the automated slaughtering and preparation will spread them widely. Broilers are reared intensively in sheds, but do not seem to have attracted the amount of criticism levelled at the egg-laying procedures.

A typical broiler unit could contain as many as ten enormous sheds, each harbouring 40,000 growing birds. On eight occasions each year, the one– or two-day-old chicks arrive in a lorry from the hatchery and are then fed in gloom for the next 42 days, by which time there will hardly be sufficient space for each bird to move. Perhaps as many as ten per cent die during the rearing; the corpses may be pecked at until decomposition sets in. With eight successive 'crops' from each shed, the total yield of broilers is around three million per year.

Very large lorries are needed to deliver the feed and carry away the chickens. Some of the feed contains the bone meal fraction from rendered offal, including remains of earlier chickens, such as heads, intestines and feathers.

The thousands of tons of droppings and rotting carcasses may have to be piled high outside the sheds in preparation for distribution onto the land in between crops. Bacteria such as salmonella will inevitably abound in these heaps. Vermin, notably rats, are attracted, breed and multiply, and spread these bacteria widely. Birds, too, will feed off this debris, and there is also the possibility—apparently within the law—of it being fed to animals such as pigs or cattle. Salmonella may also spread through air.

The local water will be polluted by nitrates and nitrites as a result of these chemicals being present in high concentrations in the droppings, and seeping through soil into the nearby water channels. The ground of the site is usually low-lying and subject to flooding, so that the likelihood of excessive amounts of nitrates contaminating the drinking water is increased. The worry over nitrates is that they can be changed to other nitrogen-containing chemicals which may cause cancer in people. Already, some of our drinking water in Eastern England contains concentrations of nitrates that many people, including the European Commission, believe to be too high.

There are basically four types of egg-laying flocks. The commonest is the battery system where several hens are housed in a cage. The cages are stacked on top of each other and in long rows. Water and feed are distributed constantly, and the artificial lighting is switched on and off cyclically. When eggs are laid, these roll gently to the edge of the cage and onto conveyor belts where they are moved on for sorting, packing and grading. Certainly, concern over cruelty exists. Sometimes, as a result of feather-plucking and attempted cannibalism, the beaks have to be cut off. The issues of cruelty are well covered in Clare Druce's book *Chicken and Egg: who pays the price?* Clare Druce has been campaigning for years against the battery system. She presents an interesting argument that the whole system may be illegal. The attitude of MAFF is, not surprisingly, seen to be belligerent and arrogant.

The second type of egg-laying production is the barn egg, and is nearly as intensive—that is, based on the number of birds per square metre—as battery production. In barn eggs the cages are replaced by perches and egg-laying boxes are provided. There is still an enormous number of birds crammed into a dimly lit shed.

Free range eggs come really as two types. The commonest, which is fundamentally dishonest but strictly within the definition of 'free range', keeps the laying flock on the floor of a large shed, the birds being fed much as in other systems. An entrance leads to a small pen outside. How many birds venture outside or for how long, is anyone's guess. The point is that the amount of food obtained by foraging in the tiny pen must be limited indeed. This system has been described as 'pseudo-free-range'. Finally, there is the real free range with all the food provided outside in runs; some of the food may be given as meal, etc., but a substantial portion of the hen's diet will be obtained by foraging and eating wild material. The return to the hen house occurs only at night or for egg-laying (hopefully!). These are the farmyard hens.

Salmonella in Eggs

The argument over the extent to which, or indeed whether, eggs are contaminated at all, still seems to rage. The evidence as seen by myself is quite clear: there was, and still is, a problem. First, let us look at the structure of an egg. The shell looks solid but it is not. There are numerous tiny holes all over it. These are invisible to the naked eye. Under the microscope, these holes or pores can be seen to be plugged; but fairly loosely. One reason that eggs should not be washed is that these plugs can be dissolved away, so permitting a greater risk of bacteria getting in, or more water vapour escaping. Inside the egg-shell there are two thin membranes, normally clinging to each other with no actual space in between. Inside the membranes is the egg white, which mainly consists of water and a protein, albumen. When these are heated the albumen molecule is altered, so that it cannot dissolve in water. This results in a white precipitate and explains why cooking the egg makes the albumen white.

Also present in the white is a mixture of substances that either kill bacteria or at least stop them increasing in number. The best known of these chemicals is lysozyme, which is also found in human tears and provides a natural defence against bacteria getting into our eyes. The yolk does not appear to possess these substances. At one end of the egg the membranes inside the shell separate to hold a volume of air, one of whose functions is to provide a cushion effect for the growing chick if sudden force is applied to the shell.

Air is capable of passing in and out of the egg, and water vapour can escape outwards. But the intact egg has normally been considered free of bacteria, and ideally it certainly should be. It is intended to provide a safe environment for the developing chick, yet it will also permit diffusion of air inwards, of which oxygen is the most important component, and the diffusion of waste gases outwards.

There are two ways that bacteria can get inside an egg. Until recently, the best known method was through shell contamination and damage, usually after laying. Many people have experienced a real 'bad egg'. On cracking the shell, a revolting sulphurous smell from gases suggests that something is definitely amiss. The egg white and yolk may be obviously discoloured, possible grey or black or greenish, or even pink. Sometimes the boundary between the white and the yolk has disappeared altogether. Such a bad egg will have been caused by bacteria getting in through the shell, somehow defeating all the natural barriers—the plugged shell pores, the two membranes, and the chemicals in the white. Strangely enough, the bacteria which do this tend not to be salmonella, but less dangerous types found mainly in the soil. On no account should these eggs be eaten, however, since nasty chemicals could have been created as a result of growth of the bacteria in the egg.

The most obvious means by which these bacteria can get into the egg is through droppings or soil being rubbed into a crack or other blemish. A largish shell crack could also rupture the membranes, and large numbers of bacteria could overcome the effects of the natural antibacterial chemicals in the white. This is the basis of sound advice for eggs: avoid buying any with major cracks or which are badly soiled. Also, remember that eggs should not be washed, as there is a risk of the soiling materials being forced through the pores to the inside.

Sometimes salmonella enters an egg through the shell. If this has happened, it may not be quite so obvious as with other bacteria. When salmonella grows in an egg it generally doesn't produce abnormal colours or very unpleasant gases and smells. The main effect is a cloudiness which could be missed.

Shell contamination has been known for years and many of the procedures in operation today are aimed to keep it to a minimum. The battery cages are designed to let the egg roll away from the hens' feet and droppings. Inspection during sorting at packing stations should identify risky eggs so that they can be discarded. The retailer may also check—although the trend towards cling-film wrapping of the egg box will make this difficult—and the consumer should now be aware of the risks with cracked or soiled eggs.

All these factors argue that the incidence of contamination of the inside of the egg from the shell should be on the decline. There is, of course, no proof, nor indeed scientific evidence, which would be exceedingly costly to obtain.

Before discussing the other known form of egg contamination, the 'transovarian' method by which the bacteria gain access directly to the egg yolk, we must look at the natural occurrence of salmonella bacteria. These were named after an American, Dr Salmon, and have nothing to do with fish! Just four different types of these cause enteric fevers, or typhoid in humans. These spread from one person to another, usually through water or food. They do not come from animals. They are a problem, particularly where quality of water is not up to standard, but do not concern us here.

There are about 2,000 other types of salmonella. These have one or more natural hosts in which they can live without necessarily causing disease—chickens, ducks, turkeys, other birds, many mammals, and reptiles are examples. Each of these 2,000 salmonella can have a different host range: some may be able to infect just one or two hosts, whereas others can involve a wide variety. The severity of any resulting illness also varies. The next complicating factor is that the salmonella can be transferred from its natural host to almost any food as a result of lapses in food hygiene. For example, bean sprouts can become contaminated with salmonella although there is no suggestion that these are the natural host! It is the intestines of animals and birds that are the natural reservoir, and provide the potential for spread of the bacteria.

Let's look at some particular salmonella species. *Salmonella typhimurium* used to be the commonest type causing illness in humans. It is found in almost all our food animals and birds, and is said to have a broad host range. Indeed, it causes disease in many animals. *Salmonella pullorum* caused havoc in poultry flocks some years ago, but only rarely affected humans. Our recent problem salmonella is *Salmonella enteritidis*, which really only affects humans and poultry. Chickens, both broilers and egg-layers, are most commonly involved, but in these it does not cause disease that frequently. It has only occasionally been found in ducks and turkeys, and is rare in other food animals.

The two types of salmonella most likely to produce serious disease in man are therefore *Salmonella typhimurium* and *Salmonella enteritidis*. Exactly why this is so is not fully understood, but probably relates to their toxin, known as an entertoxin, which irritates our intestines through a damaging effect. It is, of course, true that many foods may be contaminated with *Salmonella enteritidis* as a result of either poultry and egg products becoming incorporated into composite foods, such as mayonnaise. Alternatively, people after recovering from the disease due to *Salmonella enteritidis* harbour it in their intestines for months, and then transfer bacteria to food through poor personal hygiene. Occasionally, the salmonella can spread between patients and staff in hospitals. This is known as cross-infection.

If several hundred people become ill with salmonella food poisoning from one locality at round about the same time, three different aspects will contribute to the scale of the outbreak and each one must be considered. One is the source of the contaminated food; the next is how it came about that so many people consumed so much contaminated food—that is, through catering errors; and the third is the possibility of spread of the infection between people.

Claims have been made that the cause of the increase of *Salmonella enteritidis* is due mainly to catering errors (for example, in North and Gorman's book *Chickengate*). Of course, these will aggravate the problem. There is no escaping the fact that chickens and eggs are the natural source of *Salmonella enteritidis*, and the phenomenal rise in its incidence between 1984 and 1988 can only be accounted for by increased contamination of food, most probably eggs.

The year 1984 saw our two biggest salmonella outbreaks. One was well publicised—that in Stanley Royd hospital, with 455 cases and 19 deaths. The British Airways outbreak of 766 cases and two deaths was not, but was the first major problem with *S.enteritidis* type 4 which has been the particular sub-type most commonly associated with eggs and poultry.

Between 1983 and 1988, the number of cases of *Salmonella enteritidis* officially reported increased about fifteen-fold, from around 1,000 to 15,000 cases per year. Our notification system is inefficient: partly because not all patients visit their doctor, not all doctors arrange a laboratory test, not all tests will be found to be positive, and not all positives will be reported. For this reason, many people use a multiplier to estimate the real figures. The Americans use a factor of about a hundred-fold; we prefer a ten-fold factor. This converts the number of egg (and to a lesser extent chicken) associated *Salmonella enteritidis* to 150,000 for 1988, or about 3,000 per week.

Since 1989, the method of reporting has changed, so that it is difficult to be certain of the trend. Probably the numbers have flattened off, although the problem is by no means solved.

The scale of the salmonella problem has been quite remarkable, but is not confined to the United Kingdom. Similar bacteria have been prevalent in many European countries. One quarter of the salmonella cases in Leeds during 1988 were brought back from holiday—mainly Spain, Portugal and France. These appeared to be identical to the strains from this country.

A number of considerations suggest that contaminated broiler meat cannot be the main explanation for the fifteen-fold rise in salmonella food poisoning. First, for twenty years or more, it has been known that 50-80 per cent of raw chickens are contaminated with salmonella. This has not changed recently and cannot in itself be the cause of the increase. Secondly, might the answer lie in the greater consumption of chicken? The amount of chicken eaten has increased by about 50 per cent in the last ten years; this cannot account for the fifteen-fold rise. Thirdly, perhaps our hygiene in the home, institutions, catering, has deteriorated so much as to explain the increase. There is no evidence for this; indeed the number of outbreaks in hospitals seems to be declining. Fourthly, how can we account for the observation that the number of cases of *Salmonella typhimurium* remained virtually unchanged between 1983 and 1988, while *Salmonella enteritidis* rose fifteen-fold? No other type of salmonella increased to this extent. The natural habitat of *Salmonella enteritidis* is predominantly only chickens and eggs, and we have excluded broilers as the major cause of the rise. This leaves eggs, and the detailed evidence is discussed below.

Transovarian Contamination of Eggs
'Transovarian' means that the salmonella passes directly from the ovaries—the egg-laying organs—to the egg, mainly in the yolk, as the egg is being formed. This has been considered in previous years, and the idea is therefore not completely new. However, its importance certainly is. There are four lines of evidence in favour of it.

1 Salmonella has been identified within the intact egg. This has been the case even when inspection of the shell showed no cracks or damage. Moreover, before the

detection for salmonella, the outside of the shell was cleaned with spirit to prevent any bacteria getting into the egg from the shell during the opening of the egg.

2 The ovaries and other internal organs of the laying hen have been found to contain salmonella. It is important to note that many of these birds were laying quite normally.

3 Experiments have shown that deliberately feeding laying hens with *Salmonella enteritidis* in their meal can result in the bacteria appearing in the internal organs.

4 There really is no alternative explanation for the dramatic rise in *Salmonella enteritidis* numbers.

It has been argued that this evidence cannot in itself account for the problem. For example, North and Gorman state that it is impossible for eggs to contain enough salmonella to cause food poisoning. This notion seems to be based on the experiments of about 40 years ago on prison volunteers in the United States, who were fed increasing numbers of salmonellae until they developed symptoms. In these people, it is true that as many as 100 million bacteria were needed. But in the young and the elderly there is very good reason to think that far fewer bacteria are needed to cause illness. Moreover, the fatty nature of the egg yolk could protect the bacteria from destruction by acid in the stomach. A similar example occurred with food poisoning from *Salmonella napoli* in chocolate, when only a few hundred bacteria were needed to cause disease. The fat in the chocolate presumably was responsible for protecting the bacteria against acid destruction. North and Gorman also suggest that there may not be enough oxygen present in an egg to support the presence of large numbers of salmonellae. But salmonella can grow to quite large numbers in the absence of oxygen, and in any case some oxygen must diffuse into the egg, otherwise the chicken would not grow.

This seems to be the main thrust of the argument denying that there is a new salmonella problem. The real difficulty for scientists is that absolute proof is impossible to obtain for each case of food poisoning: it would be necessary to demonstrate the presence of salmonella in the egg yolk and in the organs of the laying hen and then show that the egg, after being eaten, caused illness. The obvious difficulty arises when it is appreciated that most eggs are consumed in total, and any shell remnant is unlikely to have yolk adhering to it. Since boxes of battery eggs do not show the identity of the farm where they were laid, let alone the individual hen, it is impossible to trace back the egg to the hen. The fact that eggs are not compulsorily identified with their farm of origin can only be deplored.

So, transovarian spread remains the only plausible explanation for the massive rise in *Salmonella enteritidis* since 1983. What is the source of that bacteria and how can we account for its widespread distribution?

The ultimate source is likely to be the chicken feed. Propaganda statements that it might be the air, or rats or mice, or pigeons, are not helpful, since it does not tell us where these animals and birds acquired the infection in the first place. Even if *Salmonella enteritidis* was found in a rat caught within or near a battery house, the obvious interpretation would be that it had been infected by the hens, via, say, the droppings.

We have already seen that the same strain of *Salmonella enteritidis*, type 4, has been the most prevalent isolate all over Europe. Since it can pass successively from chicken to egg and hence through different generations, there is no reason to doubt that it arose in the breeding flocks abroad and then descended through several generations to laying flocks in many countries.

Consistent with this proposal is the observation that new-born chicks in their first few days or weeks of life can develop salmonella infection, and then recover. Presumably, the salmonella infected them from within the egg and, after recovery, the bacteria resided in the internal organs and ovaries to infect subsequent generations.

That the salmonella frequently co-exists with its host, the hen, suggests a particular type of biological status. If a bacterium damages its host, it is said to be a parasite; if it lives on the host without causing harm, it is a commensal, and if this relationship benefits both host and bacterium, it is said to be symbiotic. It is not possible to determine whether the relationship between the salmonella and the hen is predominantly one of symbiosis or commensalism, but we can understand how and why the epidemic developed without causing the egg producers to be aware of the problem, since there was little extra mortality in the flocks. We must assume that this relationship—whether symbiotic or commensal—resulted from the constant feeding of contaminated material, so that evolutionary pressures favoured a non-parasitic relationship between the bacteria and the hen. It is, of course, not in the 'interest' of a bacterium to kill the host—the provider of its home and its food! Indeed, there are general evolutionary pressures favouring a reduction in virulence of a dangerous infection. Tuberculosis, syphilis and influenza are not as dangerous as they once were to some populations. Such change in virulence can occur as a result of evolution in both the micro-organism and the host.

With hens and *Salmonella enteritidis* we have bred a type of bird excellent at laying brown eggs all the year round, but unfortunately possessing a predisposition to harbour salmonella. The bacteria may have evolved to encourage this relationship.

That man suffers from food poisoning due to *Salmonella enteritidis* is an accident. The control must be to manipulate the breeding flocks to be salmonella-free. Many would see little prospect of this, given that it would need to be undertaken on a European basis. Measures being implemented in this country are based on destroying infected flocks and will help to an extent, but will not reach the root of the problem—that is, presumably,

contamination in the elite flocks. Incidentally, there are
reports of some egg producers bypassing the statutory
surveillance swabs by heating the swabs in microwave
ovens.

The Number of Eggs Infected With Salmonella

It is not possible to make an exact estimate of the
proportion of eggs contaminated with salmonella. Based
on the number of cases of the disease in the human
population and the numbers of eggs eaten, it is of the
order of one in 5,000 to one in 10,000. Certainly the degree
of contamination is not uniform. Bad hygiene in certain
farms could well aggravate the problem, as might the
number of eggs currently being imported. Any one person
might consider that one in 5,000 is unimportant, as it will
take the average individual consumer fifteen years to eat a
contaminated egg! Fair enough. But look at it another way:
suppose there are five million elderly and young
vulnerable people, and each eats one egg a day, then a
thousand vulnerable people will put themselves at risk
each day. This is not acceptable. We have to endeavour to
eliminate salmonella from eggs.

The advice first presented to the public by the
government during 1988 still stands: *do not eat any raw egg.*
This should include the yolk, which is raw unless it is hard
all the way through. So boiled eggs need seven to ten
minutes; fried eggs should be cooked on both sides until
the yolk is hard. It is difficult to cook poached eggs safely
at all. Scrambled eggs should be firm and omelettes
cooked until no runny egg is left. Similarly, soufflés and
baked eggs should be firm.

In conclusion, there is no reason why a salmonella-free
breeding flock could not be established. Care over the feed
and the prevention of infection from other outside sources
would be required. This, coupled with a continued
surveillance of laying flocks, should reduce the incidence
of salmonella contamination. Until this is achieved,

caution with eggs will be required. The price to pay for the consumer will be small, but surely well worth it.

The decontamination of broilers at the point of sale poses a remarkable challenge. Even if salmonella-free flocks were established, the problem of campylobacter would remain since it is found normally in chickens' intestines. It is certainly true that free range broilers are preferable to intensively-reared birds from the point of view of quality and welfare, but care will probably still have to be exercised in their storing and cooking.

TABLE 6

Types of chicken-rearing for commercial purposes

Intensive rearing of chicken for meat,
 not eggs (broilers).
Pseudo-free-range chicken.
Genuine free range chicken.
Battery egg production.
Barn egg production.
Pseudo-free-range egg production.
Genuine free range egg production.

Imported eggs.

TABLE 7

Salmonella contamination of eggs

1 Contamination through the shell
  Uncommon.
  Known for many years.
  Associated with shell damage and dirt.
  Should be declining because of the exclusion of defective eggs from sale.

2 Transovarian spread
  Uncommon, until recent years.
  Mainly due to Salmonella enteriditis type 4.
  Occurs all over Europe, and possibly in all other continents, including USA.
  Capable of causing food poisoning.
  Probably originates in breeding flocks from feed.
  Thorough cooking of eggs still needed.

5 Food Irradiation

Many of the issues created by the government's proposal to authorise food irradiation have been well aired. Two, however, have not been discussed adequately: the reasons underlying the intention to permit irradiation, and the fact that the technique is essentially an unsatisfactory method of food preservation.

The Process

All electromagnetic energy, whether gamma rays, electron beams, ultraviolet light, X-rays or visible light, has damaging effects on bacteria and viruses, but little effect on the agents that cause BSE and similar diseases. A number of different types of irradiation can be used to eliminate micro-organisms from food, including particles such as electrons, or X-rays. Electron beams are used in France, but it is expected that gamma rays will be the chosen method in the United Kingdom. Since gamma rays generate electrons on collision, the two types of irradiation are not substantially different.

For the sterilisation of surgical equipment and devices, Cobalt 60 is currently being used as a source of the gamma rays. It is interesting that our approach in the Health Service is to use irradiation for sterilising purposes only where the simpler, safer and cheaper options are not feasible, due, for example, to the risk of damage to an instrument by heat or certain gases.

So for food, radioactive Cobalt 60 will be mainly used. This isotope spontaneously disintegrates to the non-radioactive Nickel 60, with a half-life of 5.27 years—that is, after this length of time the potency of the irradiation is half what it was, after 10.54 years a quarter, and so on. This is a fairly long half-life, with an advantage that the isotope should not need to be replaced very often. However, if any accidental contamination did occur, the radioactivity would persist for a long time. When each atom of Cobalt 60 converts to Nickel 60, an event seemingly incapable of being stopped or influenced, three electro-magnetic emissions result. One of these is a β-particle or electron with an energy of up to 0.31 MeV (that is, million electron-volts). This particle penetrates poorly and is unimportant. The other two products are gamma rays or photons with energies of 1.17 and 1.33 MeV. These rays emanate randomly from the radioactive source; they are incredibly narrow, so that they actually penetrate the food substance within its molecules. They move in straight lines until colliding with the outside shell of an atom, but are not deflected by impact. At the point of collision, the gamma ray is dissipated; electrons, and then a whole series of new chemicals are produced in the immediate area of each collision. Free radicals, the potentially dangerous chemicals created by the breaking up of molecules, are formed, but only temporarily, as a result of their conversion by other chemical changes into more inert compounds.

For two reasons, parts of an object closest to the radiation source receive more irradiation than those that are farthest away. The more important is due to the physical law known as the inverse square law, which states that the exposure to irradiation varies inversely with the square of the distance from the source. This occurs because the farther away the object is from the source, the greater is the chance of the ray missing. To give a specific example: if the dose received by an object one inch from a source is 3.0 kiloGrays, then the dose received two inches distant will be 3.0 divided by 2^2 or 0.75 kiloGrays. The kiloGray is the unit of irradiation that produces 1,000 joules per kilogram, or about a rise in temperature of one sixth of a degree centigrade. The energy from the photon is translated finally into heat.

The other reason for uneven exposure to irradiation is that once a gamma ray has collided with an atom, it will be destroyed, and unable to penetrate farther. So most collisions are likely to occur near to the source. However, this effect is not as marked as with the loss of available photons according to the inverse square law.

The net result of these two factors is that the dose of irradiation an item receives, particularly a large item near to the source, is quite variable. This can be overcome to an extent by irradiating an item from both sides, but even so the effect is not uniform. The most consistent dose of irradiation is achieved by exposing a small item a long distance away from the source. This means that much of the irradiation is wasted, and it increases the cost, danger and inconvenience. In practice, were an entire chicken to be exposed to an average dose of 3.0 kiloGrays, it could mean an actual dose from say 4.5 on the surface to 1.5 at the centre. This uneven potency remains one of the chief problems of irradiation and is particularly important for the many foods where the margin between the dose needed to destroy micro-organisms and that liable to cause unpleasant tastes, etc., is very narrow.

Another unsatisfactory feature of the process is that it is discontinuous, with each collision of photon with atoms causing focal 'chemical explosions', quite unlike other types of food preservation where the preservative is applied continuously throughout the whole product. Some very small micro-organisms such as bacterial spores may be relatively resistant to irradiation, owing to the simple probability that the rays may miss them.

If bacteria are present in the food, it is thought that they are killed by gamma rays in the following way (no one has actually seen this happen; the evidence is indirect): it is thought that the 'chemical explosion' induced by the collision between the gamma ray and an atom causes damage to the bacterial DNA. DNA is a large molecule with the sections joined by links between a sugar and a phosphate molecule. It is thought that these links are literally broken so that the DNA cannot function. Under most conditions DNA exists as two strands coiled together, and this damage can occur in one or both strands. However, bacteria are pretty resistant to the effects of irradiation. This is the problem. The doses needed to kill them reliably may cause unpleasant-tasting chemicals to be formed. This toughness shown by bacteria is due to their ability to repair their damaged DNA. For example, the hole in one strand of DNA can be repaired by using the intact other strand as a type of template and the bacteria's own enzymes.

Research in many countries has shown that bacteria vary enormously in their ability to be destroyed by irradiation. Those most easily removed are known as the food spoilage bacteria. Most of us have memories of buying an out-of-date chicken or other food item, or keeping it too long and noticing either a nasty 'off' smell or else green discoloration, sometimes slimy. These effects are caused by the growth of these spoilage bacteria. One that is frequently encountered is known as pseudomonas. If these were eaten, they would be expected to have an unpleasant taste, but they would not cause any illness. The real problem with these bacteria is they can grow when the temperature is fairly cold, so even in chilled conditions in supermarkets, they can be troublesome if the item is stored for too long. However, for the consumer they are an invaluable guide to the safety or wholesomeness of food. If these bacteria are present in large numbers, so might others be, including some dangerous ones. Unfortunately, most of the dangerous bacteria themselves, or their poisons or toxins, do not have any smell, taste or colour, so it is these harmless food spoilage bacteria that alert us to the possibility that the food should not be eaten—in other words it is bad. Irradiation can easily remove these warning bacteria.

Other bacteria that are relatively vulnerable to irradiation include salmonella and campylobacter, two of the notorious causes of food poisoning. These, certainly the majority of them, are killed by doses of about 0.2-0.5 kiloGrays. But other bacteria, which may be present and can either be harmless, or possibly dangerous, need doses of 1-5 kiloGrays for destruction. Others are even more resistant. Some bacteria are able to survive hostile environments, such as drying, by packaging their essential components into a tiny resilient sphere. This is known as a spore and is able to resist all manner of physical agents, such as heat, drying, chemicals and irradiation. We must consider one particular problem bacterium. It is known as *Clostridium botulinum* and when actively growing can produce a powerful poison that causes the disease botulism. Fortunately, for growth to occur it needs exacting conditions, including the exclusion of oxygen in the air. The food industry has appreciated this danger, and until recently has taken a very responsible attitude by using processing methods that were not liable to permit the growth of this bacterium. If problems did occur, they were the results of unfortunate and rare accidents, such as the defective canned salmon eaten in Birmingham in 1978.

Unfortunately the spores of *Clostridium botulinum* need doses of gamma rays of between 10-25 kiloGrays to eliminate them. These spores are fairly widespread, for example in soil, on some vegetables and on some fish and meat. Before you get alarmed by this, it should be appreciated that these spores themselves do not cause disease and if there is air present, they cannot change back to the growing form that can be dangerous.

The problem in irradiating food such as vacuum-packed fish should now become clear: it is not possible to use high enough doses of irradiation to eliminate the spores without causing unpleasant tastes. At lower doses, the various bacteria causing food spoilage—or the bad smell—will be killed by irradiation, but not the spores of *Clostridium botulinum*. It is well known that remaining bacteria may grow to large numbers if others competing for space and nutrients are removed first. This explains why the surface of the human body and our intestines are teeming with bacteria—to help deter unpleasant micro-organisms. Moreover, if irradiation is used to prolong the keeping quality of food (or shelf life), then there are two powerful factors favouring the survival of these spores and their possible conversion to dangerous forms. Experiments have shown that the combination of irradiation and prolonged storage can indeed encourage the growth of *Clostridium botulinum*. This, it must be stressed, is only likely to be a problem where air is excluded, such as in vacuum packs. But air (or rather oxygen) can sometimes be neutralised by chemicals, say in the centre of meat pies or even by other bacteria, possibly introduced after irradiation.

The encouragement of the growth of *Clostridium botulinum* presents the greatest hazard with irradiation, at least from a bacterial point of view. Some reassurance might be provided by the knowledge that in addition to exclusion of air, this bacterium needs an adequate temperature for growth. Refrigeration should prevent most types from growing, but one type can grow down to temperatures as low as +3.3⁰C. It is exceedingly difficult always to ensure refrigeration temperatures at this or below; on the open supermarket shelves this would hardly be possible at all.

So far, in describing the process of irradiation of food, I have described some very obvious and important snags. They are an intrinsic part of the process; they do not arise because of misuse or accidents, but because the process is not a satisfactory food preservative. To summarise: the dose which any region of a food item receives is variable; there are discontinuous or point effects; the margin between doses needed to kill micro-organisms and those that cause nasty tastes may be too small; bacteria are too variable in their vulnerability to it; and the 'desirable' food spoilage bacteria are most sensitive whilst the dangerous *Clostridium botulinum* are most resistant. We can add five more inevitable snags:

1 Transient Effect

The exposure of a food item to irradiation occurs briefly, over seconds or minutes, whilst other methods of preserving food exert their effect over the duration of the life of the product. Consider all the well-researched and tested methods of preservation: drying, salting, pickling, sugaring, canning and deep-freezing. These are applied right throughout the storage life of the product. With irradiation, it is hoped that this brief experience will produce a lasting effect. We have seen, however, that subsequent storage may merely cause alterations in the proportions of various bacteria, not their elimination or certain prevention of their growth. The traditional methods of preservation all prevent bacterial growth. Moreover, in practical terms, it will be impossible to ensure that irradiated food will not be rewrapped or processed or abused in a number of ways after treatment.

2 Packaging Chemicals

Because of the worry over bacterial contamination after irradiation, any treated item must be securely wrapped and the gamma rays must inevitably react with this wrapping, generating new chemicals that in turn could contaminate the food. This is a theoretical danger, but hardly any research has been done on it. Gamma rays can produce some dramatic effects on containers: transparent plastic polycarbonate may go yellow after exposure, and colourless glass can go grey or even blackish! It is, incidentally, easy to incorporate an indicator into any packaging that will show whether the product has been irradiated. The problem is that such packing could be replaced by the unscrupulous.

3 Resistance of Toxins

Poisons or toxins are produced by certain food poisoning bacteria. These substances, if present in food, can cause serious illness on their own. So whilst irradiation might destroy the bacteria that had produced the toxins, if those toxins are still present, the food is still dangerous. These toxins are proteins which are resistant to irradiation. It follows from this that if a food consignment (for example, prawns) is found on routine testing to be heavily contaminated with a variety of bacteria and toxins, irradiation can be used to remove the obvious evidence of contamination—the whole bacteria—but will leave behind the toxins which, whilst they are still capable of causing illness, will be difficult to detect. Despite claims to the contrary, irradiation can be used irresponsibly to 'clean up' dirty food.

4 Recovery of Exposed Bacteria

This problem is only just beginning to be appreciated. Some bacteria, additional to those capable of causing botulism, can recover and multiply during the days after treatment with gamma rays. Those in question are active at low temperatures and will be considered in detail in Chapter 7. Listeria is one of them, and if irradiation was used regularly for prolonging the shelf-life of chicken, it could actually increase the amount of contamination with that bacterium by the time that the chicken was purchased.

5 Loss of Nutrients

Irradiation necessitates a journey to and from the irradiating plant, which inevitably must increase the age of the product by the time of sale. If retailers then keep the item for longer than usual, the extra age could have an important deleterious effect on nutrients and vitamins. In any case, there will already have been some loss incurred by the exposure to irradiation itself. Of the vitamins, the net loss of Vitamin C and folic acid might be considerable, and of other substances, the polyunsaturated fatty acids would be liable to decompose.

This extra step in the already complex and lengthy food chain must contribute to general risks from accidents, mistakes, etc.—for example, breakdown of the refrigeration plant in lorries and stores, use of the wrong dose of gamma rays and possible accidents at the plants with risks to staff. It would, however, only be an extreme calamity that could cause transfer of radioactivity to the food itself.

Irradiation is therefore quite clearly an unsatisfactory method of preservation or decontamination of many items. This explains why, despite research for most of this century, its potential use, benefits and advantages are still subject to much debate. Those sections of the food industry enthusiastic for the process presumably intend to use it to prolong shelf life of, say, poultry or even to clean up contaminated food. These enthusiasts have attempted to divert the issue to one between responsible independent scientists who support the process and emotional consumers who oppose it through ignorance. This is not the real issue at all. The basic process is inherently unsatisfactory, except perhaps for a tiny range of items. Its use can never be extensive. It is in a way a giant red herring; it will have little impact on our society , except perhaps as a factor contributing to the lack of confidence in MAFF.

History of Irradiation of Food and Other Products
I am indebted in this section to J. F. Diehl's *Safety of Irradiated Foods.* Whilst not agreeing with his general conclusions, I find his book an excellent account of the attempts to use irradiated food so far. *Food Irradiation* by Tony Webb and Tim Lang puts the issues very much from

the consumer perspective and is also highly recommended.

Seemingly the first use of irradiation to control an infestation (that is, in the broadest sense) was about 75 years ago in the United States, to prevent damage to cigars by beetle attack. Usually, the more complicated a living organism is, the more vulnerable it is to damage by irradiation of any type; the beetle can therefore be destroyed by low doses of irradiation. In fact, X-rays were used.

During the next few decades, it became clear that X-rays would provide too low a dose for bacteria, so gamma rays were researched in the United States, France, Belgium and other European countries. The first commercial use was in Germany in 1957, against parasites in spices. As with tobacco, exceptionally low doses could be used. There is, however, no need to use irradiation for preserving spices; steam treatment can be effective. In 1960, irradiation was used in Canada to prevent potatoes from sprouting. Again, because of the relative complexity of plant structures, a low dose could be used, and again, other methods are available to prevent potatoes from sprouting. In the 1970s, irradiation of animal feeds was introduced into a number of Third World countries. One of the problems with a warm, moist climate is that it encourages growth of fungi, some of which produce unpleasant if not dangerous toxins. In the absence of alternative methods, such use may have some justification.

Today, about thirty countries permit irradiation for the following foods: spices, cocoa powder, dehydrated foods, deep-frozen foods, gum arabic, onions (to prevent sprouting), potatoes, dehydrated mushrooms, chicken meat, flour, egg powder, frozen poultry, prawns, frogs' legs, fresh fruit, fish and fermented sausages (that is, salami-type products). Many countries permit just one or two uses, such as for spices.

Several items on this list are supposedly already preserved. It is difficult to justify the use of irradiation for the dried items—cocoa powder, dehydrated foods, mushrooms, flour, and egg powder; surely the need for irradiation denotes incompetence in basic hygiene in preparation or storage of the products. Similarly, the need to irradiate deep-frozen foods is quite inexplicable. Prawns, frogs' legs, and boned chicken meat are amenable to irradiation because of their small size, but surely the process is not needed—unless it is being used to clean up contaminated food, a procedure denied by MAFF. It is true that low doses can prevent onions from sprouting, but is this really a problem? Are there not other adequate methods of preserving onions? Fish, too, can be preserved so easily by deep-freezing, and there is no reason to irradiate fermented sausages—a process itself designed to preserve—unless the hygiene control is abysmal.

The use of irradiation for fresh fruit is puzzling. Whilst it may delay spoilage by fungal growth for a few days, there seems no problem at present in the United Kingdom in obtaining fresh fruit.

It seems quite evident that irradiation is not needed. It is generally being used to rescue a tiny range of contaminated foods which should have been prepared and stored with good hygiene, but were not.

Irradiation in Practice in the United Kingdom

During publicity over food irradiation, two explanations have been put forward by MAFF and the food industry to justify its use: to destroy food-poisoning pathogens and to extend the shelf life of certain products. The emphasis has subtly shifted from the first to the second, with many commentators pointing out that the chief causes of food poisoning will not be eliminated by the use of irradiation. For example, shell eggs cannot be irradiated because of the formation of nasty tastes in the yolk and the running of the white into the yolk. Cheese, too, is unsuitable because of its high fat content, as are composite meals. Moreover, food poisoning often results from hygiene errors in institutions, restaurants, take-aways and in the home (the latter probably not common).

So in reality, irradiation might be used for the convenience of possibly just one supermarket chain to store chicken products for a few days longer than hitherto. Is this really worth all the fuss?

Uses of Irradiation

In practice, irradiation might be used in a dose of say 3.0 kGy for treating certain foods. It is not in doubt that some bacteria, including salmonella, would be eliminated by this exposure. The problems would be generated by two general consequences of irradiation—the production of novel chemicals in the food, and how irradiation might be used or abused in practice. Statements from ministers that 'irradiation is safe' are evidently silly: we do not know whether harmful chemicals are generated in the food, and the *way* that irradiation is used will determine safety or damage.

Toxic Chemicals in Food

Inevitably even low dose irradiation will generate new chemicals in food, particularly free radicals and derivations from fatty acids. Free radicals themselves only last transiently, but these highly active chemicals will generate a whole series of novel chemicals, which in turn may undergo further reactions on storage. Cooking will also have the opportunity to accelerate the formation of further novel molecules. At the moment, little is known about these substances, and there is no evidence to indicate whether such molecules might be safe or dangerous. Indeed, many novel foods or processes also present indefinable risks. What is disturbing, however, is to hear statements from protagonists of food irradiation to the effect that 'many patients, such as those with immunosuppression, have eaten irradiated food without ill effects!' Or 'irradiated food has been in use for thirty years in thirty countries without any problem'. The truth is that few foods have been consumed after irradiation in any one country, and there are very few published studies on people who have consumed irradiated food, either in the short or in the long term. The food industry claims a study has been performed in China. This information, if it really does exist, is hardly relevant to the United Kingdom.

One disturbing study by Srikantia in India identified abnormal DNA in cells of malnourished children fed with irradiated wheat (see Webb and Lang, p.233). This study has been criticised because the control group were surprisingly 'normal', but it is worrying. The reasons why this study has not been repeated are puzzling indeed.

If irradiated food does produce chemicals harmful to us, the effects, such as the provocation of cancer, are likely to be in the long term, and it is seemingly unethical to perform any research. We can take one of two attitudes towards a technique which is not needed:

Either because we cannot tell whether or not a process is dangerous, we should assume it is safe;

Or because we cannot tell whether or not a process is dangerous, we should assume it is dangerous.

The issue is thus essentially one of philosophy, not of science. Not surprisingly, the government's Advisory Committee on irradiation spent several years arguing the issue.

There have been no studies performed on the safety of irradiated food in people outside the United States, China or India. Whilst many people in Europe may already have eaten irradiated food, some unwittingly, the effects on them have not been researched.

The American study was done on conscientious objectors over two weeks in 1953. There appeared to be no immediate hazard—which is not surprising—but no long-term follow-up studies were made.

Animal experiments have revealed conflicting information and really do not contribute much to the debate, because of their artificiality.

As far as human safety is concerned, then, there are absolutely no data that can be used to reassure anxious people. The only sensible approach must be to avoid these products altogether. There is no need to eat food treated with gamma rays.

To summarise, treatment of food with gamma rays is an unsatisfactory food preservative, has not been adequately researched, has little potential use, and will in practice do little to eliminate food poisoning. Its practical value is to the food industry—to increase the age of chickens in the supermarket. This is hardly of benefit to the consumer.

TABLE 8

Irradiation is an unsatisfactory food preservative

Food exposed only briefly to preservative.

Variable dose, particularly with large items.

Clostridium botulinum and *Listeria mono-cytogenes* relatively resistant.

Many foods not suitable for treatment.

Elimination of harmless bacteria that give warning of danger.

Possible dangerous chemicals created from packaging.

Food poisoning toxins not destroyed.

Can be used to clean up dirty food.

Food will become older by time of purchase, with loss of nutrients.

Human safety has not been, and cannot be, tested.

Unnecessary.

Will do little to reduce food poisoning.

Could increase risk of botulism and listeriosis.

Environmentally deleterious.

6 Bovine Spongiform Encephalopathy (BSE)

Most people first heard of BSE as 'mad cow disease'. This easily remembered description is not really accurate, since it places too much emphasis on the effect of the disease in damaging the cow's intellect. Perhaps 'nervous', 'anxious', or 'twitchy' cow disease would have been a more accurate description, although not so compelling. BSE has also been many people's introduction to a whole group of new diseases, or at least those that are newly described, resulting from a particularly sinister type of infectious agent.

The most well-known infectious agents are bacteria. These are relatively large, but still invisible to you and me. They can grow quickly, but can be destroyed by thorough cooking. Salmonella is a good example. They are free living; this means that they can grow in food and do not need the human body's cells in which to multiply. Viruses are smaller, generally somewhat tougher, although still capable of being destroyed by heat and chemicals, but they cannot grow in food, needing cells in which to live. Herpes, influenza and measles are examples.

Even smaller than the viruses are the infectious agents that cause BSE and similar diseases. How small, no one knows for certain, since not one has been measured. We know that they exist because the infections that they cause can be transmitted from one animal to another. They used to be called slow viruses because, after infection with them, many months or years may elapse before the disease occurs. In the scientific world, no one really knows what to call them, because even the nature of their chemical composition is unknown, except that the major substance is likely to be tightly packed, or hardened, protein. So in these pages I refer to these minuscule horror particles as simply 'infectious agents'. The alarm that they have caused results primarily from their extraordinary toughness: they are resistant to most of the usual means by which bacteria and viruses are killed, and, importantly, cooking will not kill them. The next worrying feature is that whilst the diseases they cause can take many years to develop, it is not usually possible to identify which animal is infected before the final illness. The diseases so far have always been fatal and are associated with a most unpleasant death. Until the appearance of BSE, the most reassuring aspect of these infections was that the range of animals affected was mainly confined to sheep, mink, and deer. However, man too suffers from perhaps three different types of the disease, and it may occur rarely in other mammals. Cats have recently become infected for the first time. Birds or other organisms do not seem to have been infected.

The similarities in the nature of the disease in any affected animal (including man) suggest that we are dealing with one single group of infectious agents. It is to be expected that these will vary slightly in properties, according to which animal is infected. The first common property of this group is that the time between the animal being first infected and becoming ill is some years, varying from one or two in small animals to probably twenty or more in man. The course of the final disease takes some months or years and, although the infectious agent has been found in many tissues, the significant effects are due to brain damage. The brain cells that are responsible for thinking, understanding, senses and movement are destroyed, with replacement of brain tissue by holes—literally. Under the microscope, the diseased brain does look like a sponge, with many holes of variable size scattered throughout the solid material. This is why the word 'spongiform' is used. Encephalopathy denotes any disease of the brain.

To illustrate the nature of the disease, let's look at the effects on sheep, cows and on man where the major disease is known as Creutzfeldt-Jakob.

Sheep
The first definite description of Scrapie, the disease in sheep, was made in Germany in 1759, by J. G. Leopoldt. It is interesting that Scrapie has now been eliminated completely from German sheep, and recently, when a flock of sheep was exported from Britain to Germany, and just one animal was found to be infected—that is, it was shown to have the disease—the entire flock was destroyed. The reason for this mass slaughter is that when the infection is present in a flock or herd, because it is not possible to tell which ones are infected but not yet ill, it has to be assumed that all might be.

Scrapie is thought to have been prevalent in many countries, including Britain, for at least 200 years. The disease is said to be commonest in Iceland. The reason for this is not known, but one idea is that the infectious agent may persist well on the almost soil-less volcanic lava. Apart from Germany, there is also no Scrapie in New Zealand sheep. One worrying observation is described from Iceland, where attempts were made in the earlier part of this century to rid a flock of Scrapie altogether. The entire flock was destroyed, and new stock was introduced from a locality where there was thought to have been no Scrapie previously. Within a few years, the disease appeared in the new flock and was as frequent as before. Although not the only explanation for this, it is possible that the new infections could have resulted from the persistence of the infectious agent on the ground, which then infected the animals during grazing.

When sheep become ill with Scrapie, the illness usually runs one of two different courses, although there are exceptions. The disease name, Scrapie, refers to scraping or scratching. In this form, the animal may rub its back legs with its head in a frenzied fashion. Or it may obsessively rub or scrape itself against walls, posts or trees, or indeed any object. The animal is weak, and tends to fall easily. Sheep, under normal conditions, often react positively to minor stimuli such as sudden movements. The sheep with Scrapie can show an exaggerated response to such movements. It may even seem to terrify itself by minor movements. In the other type of the disease, the reactions to stimuli tend to be more of stubbornness or refusal. The sheep may make jerky movements of its legs or ears; sometimes it may extend its head backwards, and, as may occur in all animals with this type of disease, there may be visible fine twitching or trembling of muscles. This is known as fasciculation, and cannot be controlled by the animal because it results from damage to the nerves responsible for muscle contraction. I shall return to the importance of nerve involvement later in this chapter. Sometimes the sheep walks like a donkey; this has been described as a 'cuddly trot'. Not infrequently, the infected sheep has a compulsive thirst. Fortunately, there is enough awareness of Scrapie among farmers and veterinarians for the infected animal to be recognised before it is too distressed, and put down. In the absence of any treatment, this is the only action that can be taken.

Surprisingly, the actual prevalence of Scrapie is not known in this country—itself a sad indictment of the investment into veterinary research and surveillance. Understanding of BSE would have been greatly assisted, had more studies been carried out in Scrapie in sheep and similar diseases in other animals.

Human Infection

Kuru deserves only brief mention. This occurred in the Fore tribe, a stone-age culture in the remote highlands of New Guinea. The disease occurred mainly in the first half of this century, with cases dwindling in recent years as a result of education from outside. It involved a progressive damage to the brain, many years after acquiring the infection, and chiefly affected women as a result of their cannibalistic practices, including the eating of brains after death. There are still some uncertainties as to the events leading to the disease, and what the position is today.

With the other human infection, Creutzfeld-Jakob disease (CJD), we can be more certain of some of its aspects. The two authors whose names were given to the disease described it in 1920 and 1921. It was initially called 'spastic pseudosclerosis' or 'subacute spongiform encephalopathy', and other people's names have sometimes been added to the name. Most cases are sporadic; this means they occur as 'one-offs', and do not form part of a recognised cluster of the disease or run in families. However, about fifteen per cent of affected people have had a relative suffer previously. The highest incidence is said to be in Libyan Jews living in Israel. One case has occurred in an Australian vegetarian, and this has been used by the meat industry to deny a meat source for the disease. Of course, this does nothing of the sort, since the disease could have been acquired from the mother before birth; nor is it ever possible to exclude the presence of some meat product in what is thought to be exclusively vegetarian food. The actual disease described as CJD is not always easy to diagnose, and it may not be just one illness. There is evidence that a very occasional case might be due to a genetic tendency to develop spontaneous brain damage, possibly even without the triggering effect of the infectious agent.

Most cases of CJD in men and women occur between the ages of 40 and 60 years, although a few younger people have been reported. Some of these obtained the infection through accidental injection of infected material. It is certainly possible that injection of the agent results in the more rapid development of the disease than through the more common food route. Experiments performed in animals have also suggested this.

Usually, the first symptoms of CJD are pains and uncontrolled trembling and shaking of muscles. The patient finds it difficult actually to move his hands, arms or legs to where he wants them. He may take steps that are too short or too long. His legs may feel out of control and he may stumble. He may have difficulty in keeping his eyes directed to a particular object; the eye-balls may twitch sideways uncontrollably. Sometimes the eyes may not move co-ordinately, so that two slightly different images of the same object are received; this, of course, results in double vision. Regular tremors of the hand can occur, and sometimes the limbs become rigid. Speech may be difficult, initially because of the problems in forming the words or syllables. These changes are all the result of damage to the nerve cells in the brain, which provide the control over muscle movements through the intermediary nerves.

At various stages in the disease, the effects on mental function become impaired. Three main features occur, which can predate the muscle problems and are not seen exclusively with CJD: these are depression, loss of memory, particularly for recent events, and confusion. Speech can be especially difficult because of the combination of failure to understand, failure to know what to say, and the inability to articulate words. Other activities such as writing are impeded, and eating and drinking can be difficult. Confinement to bed will sooner or later be required, leading finally to blindness, fits and incontinence of urine and faeces. The duration of the illness may be from three to nine months, or longer.

The most terrible effects of this illness have been described, intentionally, because for each person that is infected, the effect on other members of the family or the community is quite devastating.

Fortunately this disease is at present either rare or at least uncommon. Officially notified cases in the United

Kingdom have been occurring at about 30–40 per year. However, there is strong reason to believe that many cases are not diagnosed or not reported, particularly if the main presentation of the disease is one of loss of mental processes. Such patients may fade away in mental hospitals. So the real incidence of CJD is thought to be between 1,500 and 9,000 cases per year (a reference is given to this in the Bibliography).

Cattle

BSE has appeared mainly in the female of the species, because the milk-producing cow typically lives to, say, seven to ten years, whereas male beef cattle are usually slaughtered before three years of age, and veal cattle of course when very young. Since the incubation period—that is, the time between the introduction of the infectious agent into the animal and the appearance of symptoms—is thought to be about four to five years, cattle will often be slaughtered before there is a chance of the disease developing, even though some may be harbouring the infectious agent.

As farmers and veterinarians gain more experience of the disease, it is being recognised at an earlier stage than before. The animal may stand apart from the rest of the herd, it may twitch more than usual, it may be slow to respond to instructions. It appears mentally alert, at least during the first part of the disease, but can become frightened easily, and suspicious. It tends to put its feet widely apart, and the abdomen is drawn up. Walking abnormally can be an early sign. Instead of a fairly emphatic plod, it tends to overdo limb movements, and in particular any change of direction gives trouble. The hind limbs can become splayed when turning sharply, particularly on wet surfaces. It may fall (a few such pictures have been shown repeatedly on television) and injure itself. Despite apparently eating normally, the faeces become harder and the animal loses weight. The impression is that there is increased water loss from the body, and this may be a factor in causing the reduced milk yield.

Reduced milk was formerly one of the first signs, but other symptoms now usually alert the farmer to the disease. Fine muscle twitchings anywhere in the body can occur, and sometimes there are repetitive and clumsy jerks of the legs and head. The 'moo' can sound distressed and the animal may sometimes show aggression towards people and other animals.

The Epidemiology of the Disease

Which cows and cattle are infected? There have been cases among herds in England, Wales, Ireland and Scotland. However, the incidence is by no means uniform, being highest in southern England, the South West and Wales. The disease is much less common in Scotland, and apparently has not been observed at all in some herds of Highland cattle. It is most prevalent in the black and white Holstein-Friesian cattle, but these are, of course, the predominant breed. It has certainly been described in other breeds, and there is no information and no reason to suggest that some breeds are immune. Rather the variation in geographical incidence is likely to result from the differences in the use of contaminated feed derived from animal offal.

By September 1990 about 20,000 cases had been described. The total number of cattle (including cows) in the United Kingdom is of the order of twelve million. Of course, it is not known how many animals have been infected but do not appear to be suffering from the disease. Estimates of the incidence of these vary from about one to ten per cent of the total cattle population. It would have been possible to identify how many animals had been infected but were apparently healthy by studying tissues after routine slaughter. Whilst this would have been moderately costly, the failure to do this is a very damning indictment of MAFF which has attempted to justify its omission on grounds of cost alone.

The question whether this is a completely new disease or is found exclusively in the British Isles remains in dispute. What is certain is that the scale of the disease in the United Kingdom is manifestly unique. It is possible that the disease has already contaminated herds in Europe, either through the contaminated feed that was still apparently being exported to France in early 1990, or through calves born of infected cows. One attitude is that the disease is already prevalent in Europe, with the implication that any attempt to control or eliminate it in this country is futile. In practice, this possibility will mean that the pressure to control the disease will harden, and that animals in countries infected from material originating in the United Kingdom may cause their authorities to become extremely angry.

Cases of a similar disease in the United States have been described from time to time, and a disease in cows in North Yorkshire may be identical to BSE. This was known as 'stoddy' thirty or forty years ago. It is possible that the disease did occur rarely in the past, and was largely unnoticed because of its rarity. Certainly the scale of the amplification of the disease through the feed—wherever the defective agent originated—is unique to the British Isles.

The first cases were accurately described in the United Kingdom in 1986, although a few probably occurred in 1985. Careful work has identified that the source of the infection was from the rendering plants and feed producers dating from 1981–2. If it is assumed that the incubation period is typically four to five years, then it will not be known until 1991–3 whether the disease can be transmitted from cow to calf. The public have been confused by statements from MAFF: they have heard that BSE is Scrapie, but that the risk of it getting into calves is so slight that it is safe for calves from infected herds to be exported. But Scrapie is transmitted from ewe to lamb, so if BSE *is* Scrapie (which is doubtful anyway), then should this not be expected to be transmitted to calves, and why has not appropriate action been taken?

The reaction of the government to this problem was, with hindsight, predictable. It first set up a small committee, chaired by Sir Richard Southwood, none of whose members had any experience with these diseases and two of whom were retired. Their chief conclusion was that they thought (or hoped) that cattle were a 'dead-end' host; this means they thought that the disease would not spread to other hosts, including man. The words used in that report, and subsequently by MAFF, were that the risk to man was 'remote', but not a shred of evidence was presented on which to base that opinion. This will be discussed later. The Southwood Committee proposed the setting up of another committee, which was chaired by retired virologist Dr David Tyrrell who also had no experience of these agents. However, some of his members *were* experts in this field, although their public statements seemed to be in conflict with knowledge available to them. The Tyrrell committee reported in June 1989 with the advice that bovine tissues such as brain, spleen and thymus should not be used for human consumption. This report was suppressed for six months, however, during which time these organs were still being consumed by the human population. When the Tyrrell Report was finally published, in January 1990, ministers at MAFF reaffirmed that there was no danger to man from beef products, but that as a precaution these organs would not enter the food chain. The public have become confused and angry at the illogicality of this. If there is no risk, then why take any action? If there is a risk, why not take comprehensive action, since it is not known which cattle tissues may be infectious? This illogicality has continued since.

Assuming that these organs were removed because they did indeed constitute a risk, then two questions follow. First, why was action delayed for about six months, during which no important new information was gathered? Secondly, why were no attempts made early in 1990 to remove from sale products already known to contain these tissues—canned or frozen burgers, pies, sausages, and other beef items?

During the last weeks of 1989 and early in 1990, findings of spongiform encephalopathy in, first, zoo animals such as antelopes, and then domestic cats, were published, completely invalidating the Southwood Committee's hope that BSE was a 'dead-end host', that is, it would not spread beyond cattle.

The Effect on the Farming Community

Farmers were offered 50 per cent compensation by the government for each diseased cow or beef animal that was subsequently shown to be suffering from BSE. Since this sum was based on market prices, already showing some instability, it was quite inadequate, and unlikely to ensure that all suspected cattle were reported. If the animal was subsequently found not to have been suffering from BSE, then considerable financial loss might be incurred. Moreover, it would only be human nature for some farmers in possession of cows with somewhat unusual behaviour to send them to slaughter for the full market price, without the diagnosis of BSE being made and therefore reducing its value.

During the early part of 1990 the number of cows being identified as BSE-infected was around 200–300 per week, three times that of the Southwood Committee's predictions, and after the compensation was raised to 100 per cent of the market price, even more cases were reported for a time. During May 1990, following concern over the spread of BSE to cats, the media interest increased, and this resulted in many countries considering or imposing various bans on British beef and cattle. Some types of beef product were banned in schools by many Local Authorities, and this accelerated the decline in beef sales and prices.

Considerable argument raged in Europe over the safety of British beef. Most of the claims that 'beef was safe' for human consumption were made by veterinarians selected to advise the European Commission; the view of human doctors was barely sought. Why? A final compromise was reached whereby certain beef products would only be exported from the United Kingdom to other EEC countries if the cattle herd in question had had no case of BSE during the previous two years. Auction prices for beef from infected herds dropped as a consequence. This was bound to generate pressures on the farmer not to report all suspected cases of BSE, since in a previously BSE-free herd, just one case would devalue all the remaining animals.

During 1988, the government had imposed a ban on the feeding of ruminants, that is cattle and sheep, with rendered animal protein supplements. The practice of using this feed for pigs and poultry seems set to continue, however, despite severe criticism. Any BSE-infected animal could not, of course, enter the food chain at all. During the summer of 1990, the implications of these rulings were becoming evident.

Prior to the bans the rendering plants would enthusiastically purchase unwanted offal from the slaughterhouses, since the final products were in demand and profitable. Because of the reduction of demand for the protein-rich fraction, the rendering plants became unable to market all the resultant products—indeed, the generation of this substance has fallen, and most rendering plants house an enormous stock-pile of offal. The commercial attraction of offal has disappeared, so that instead of being able to charge for it, the slaughterhouses have to pay the rendering plants for its disposal. This is one factor that accounts for the continued high retail price of beef, despite reduction in the value of the whole cattle.

Another problem has been the disposal of BSE-infected carcasses due to the inadequacy of incinerator facilities. The remains have often been buried in open land-fill rubbish sites—a practice which, although within current legislation, is quite unsatisfactory because of the risk of removal of infected material by foraging animals such as cats, dogs or rodents.

The economic and social effects of reduced sales must be considerable, since the cattle not brought to auction for slaughter will continue to increase in weight and add to the cumulation of the overproduction of beef. Moreover, the cost of feeding these herds during the winter will escalate; there will be more and bigger mouths to feed and the unit price of the feed will have increased because of the offal ban.

Many farmers must feel that government action has been confused, half-hearted and of no long-term benefit to the farming community. A large number genuinely did not know the nature of the source of the feed that they had been using, or that it might carry such a risk. Members of the public were also unaware of the source of the protein supplements, otherwise they would surely have applied pressure to prevent its continuation. Why, however, were officials at MAFF, their veterinary advisers, and the makers of the feed themselves not aware of the practices? Problems of kuru and cannibalism have also been well known for some decades, as has the extreme resistance to heat of these agents, including that from sheep.

Farmers therefore have some reason to feel that they have unwittingly carried most of the damage from the BSE, through no fault of their own.

The Distribution of the Infectious Agent in Animals

Because the agent is so small and has never been pictured with certainty, not even under the electron microscope, most of what is known about this entire group of infections has been obtained from experiments in animals. If an animal is susceptible to infection by the agent, the surest and most rapid way to demonstrate infectivity is to inject infected tissues into that animal's brain. The infection can also be passed by oral feeding of infected material.

The disease in mink is thought to have been acquired accidentally in nature from Scrapie in sheep. It is very important to appreciate that once this agent has passed from sheep to mink its properties change. For example, the agent from mink can cause disease in rhesus monkeys, whilst the Scrapie agent from sheep cannot. Much of the early experimental work on Scrapie was done by Ian Pattison and colleagues, who showed that in other animals the Scrapie agent also changed in its subsequent host range and in the speed with which it induced illness. Moreover, there seemed to be some changes within the agent from different animals of the same species. This suggests that during each phase of growth in an animal the infectious particle takes on, to varying degrees, new properties derived from the most recent host. The implications for this are extremely worrying for possible human infection from BSE.

In general, about half the experiments in which animals have been deliberately injected or fed these agents have been positive: the infection has been transmitted.

For example, the causative agent of CJD has been transmitted to chimpanzees, New World monkeys, some Old World monkeys, goats, cats, mice, hamsters, and gerbils. The Scrapie agent from sheep has been transmitted to mink, just two types of monkey, goats, mice, rats, hamsters and voles. So far the agent causing BSE has been experimentally transmitted to other cows, mice, pigs, presumably cats and probably guinea pigs. Many other experiments have been started, but the results are not available because insufficient time has elapsed.

The failure to produce an infection does not mean necessarily that the infectious agent is not present in the body and cannot be passed on farther. It could simply mean that the infection does not develop into obvious illness within the lifespan of that animal.

The distribution of this type of infectious agent in sheep and mice, and also in human tissue, has been studied extensively. The following organs have all been found to contain it: brain, pituitary gland, spinal cord, nerves, spleen, adrenal gland, lymph node, thymus, lung, liver, kidney, occasionally muscle, gut, bone, and salivary gland.

Most emphatically, the disease agent is not just confined to the brain. I am in agreement with those authorities, such as Ian Pattison, who believe that we should assume the whole animal is infected.

In sheep, the first organs to be infected are the spleen, lymph node and gut, followed by the spinal cord and lung. Later, the brain and salivary gland have been found to be infectious. Finally, but still sometimes before the disease symptoms appear, yet further tissues are involved.

The distribution of the infectious agent for BSE in cattle is still largely unknown; insufficient time has elapsed for the experiments to be completed. Until all this information is available, it is reasonable to assume that most of the cattle tissues are infectious to varying extents.

The infectious agent has not been found in milk, and there is no reason to expect it to be. This must be a great reassurance, since the elderly milk-producing cow must have the greatest risk of harbouring the infectious agent. The meat from cows slaughtered at the end of their milk-production tends to be used in pies, burgers, sausages, mince and pet food rather than sold as high quality steak.

Extreme Toughness of the Infectious Agent

The resistance of this infectious agent to destruction is quite remarkable. If an evil force could devise an agent capable of damaging the human race, he would make it indestructible, distribute it as widely as possible in animal feed so that it would pass to man, programme it to cause disease slowly so that everyone would have been exposed to it before there was any awareness of its presence. The properties of these agents very nearly fit this doomsday scenario.

Much of the research into the toughness of the agents has been performed on the disease from sheep, sometimes after its transfer to mice. There is good reason to think that this group of agents is uniformly resistant to physical agents: chemicals such as domestic bleach at normal concentration do not destroy them with certainty. Enzymes in mammals' intestines known as proteinases appear to have no effect, nor enzymes that break DNA up into small pieces. Ultra-violet light and high dose gamma rays are also ineffective. The resistance to heat is most spectacular. The temperature at which red meat turns brown is around 70°C, and killing of most bacteria is easily achieved from a few seconds to a few minutes at 70°C. But the infectivity of material from CJD or Scrapie material can sometimes survive steam treatment under pressure (this is known as autoclaving) that raises the temperature to 134°C for one hour. The Scrapie agent can even survive baking in a dry oven for 24 hours at 160°C. Carleton Gajdusek and his co-workers have found that the Scrapie agent can survive in small amounts after being heated to 360°C for one hour. If meat was subjected to this treatment, it would be reduced to ashes. The only certain ways of destroying these agents are with concentrated mineral acids or alkalis, such as sulphuric acid or caustic soda; these cannot be used in practice because of their damage to containers and fabrics.

We can see now why the infectious agent for Scrapie may have persisted on the Iceland volcanic ash for many years. Some readers may recall the Scottish island which was experimentally contaminated with anthrax spores in the 1940s. This has only recently been claimed to be safe once more. The anthrax spores are tough; the causative agents for Scrapie, CJD and BSE are much, much more so.

This means that abattoirs cannot be cleansed with the usual methods, and the only safe means of disposal of infected carcasses is through careful incineration, preventing escape of unburnt material into the atmosphere, and burial of the ashes deep in the ground. Alternatively, the carcasses could be enclosed in safe shielding and buried deeply.

In both the United States and the United Kingdom, and presumably in other countries also, surgeons or other health care workers take extreme precautions when performing procedures on patients who might be, or are known to be suffering from CJD. The wearing of gloves, gowns, caps, overshoes, masks and plastic aprons are all advised. The British Veterinary Association has issued stringent guidelines for veterinary surgeons who may be about to manipulate possibly infected material.

These approaches are in stark contrast to the seeming lack of advice to abattoir workers and butchers. The practice of using the circular saw on infected carcasses, with possible generation of fine particles that enter the operator's lungs or mouth, seems extraordinary. Warnings to farmers seem also to be minimal.

It is worth restating here that, for every animal known to have BSE, many others might be harbouring the infectious agent but are seemingly not ill—at least not yet.

Can BSE Pass to Humans?

During 1990, the public were exposed to a torrent of claims from government sources that 'British beef was safe', or that any risk of humans acquiring BSE was 'remote'. These statements were made principally by representatives and ministers from MAFF and the Meat and Livestock Commission. The latter body is funded by meat sales and of course tries to defend that industry. These views seem therefore predictable. Perhaps more surprising was the claim by the Chief Medical Officer that he had consulted his expert advisers and had been told that beef was safe. It is a pity these advisers could not have been heard directly. Senior medical staff at the Department of Health must have a difficult job reconciling their requirement to enact government policy, and also to take responsibility for the health of the public. Other doctors have been more cautious. In this I do have a small amount of sympathy for the dilemma facing the official spokespeople. It would be very difficult for official statements to be made such as 'we don't know if beef is safe'. Moreover, for the claim that 'beef is safe' to be proved incorrect might take twenty years. It is certainly a supportable view that one should only issue warnings if proof of hazard has been established. The alternative view is that beef should be considered dangerous until it has been proved safe. As to which approach to take depends principally on whether one's prime concern is for the food producers or for the consumers.

In this section, I shall try and look at the factors involved in trying to establish whether beef products are safe. The first problem is the lack of information over the composition of the infective agents. We do not know for certain whether all in this group really are so similar, and it is not known how many infective particles might be needed to generate an infection in man. With other risks, we can assess mathematical likelihoods by programming computers with information. For BSE there are no data available, so this approach cannot be used. We can seemingly be confident of only one statistic—namely that the probability that humans will be infected at all from BSE lies somewhere between the extremes of zero and 100 per cent risk. This is not helpful at all. Then if the infection is capable of transfer to humans, we cannot predict how many might contract the disease, or when it would occur, or whether it would be identical to CJD.

The first question we should try to answer concerns the likely source of the infection causing the 1,500–1,900 cases of CJD per year. It must be borne in mind that because of the long incubation period of this disease, the people succumbing to it now would probably have acquired the infection in the 1960s or 1970s, or even earlier.

There is absolute proof that the infectious agent from patients suffering with CJD can be transmitted to many other animals. This is one of the standard scientific facts needed to prove that a disease is due to an infection and the principle was established by the great German microbiologist, Robert Koch. This does not mean that everyone who has a CJD-type disease acquired it by an infection, but most would be expected to have done so.

To take another example, imagine a patient who develops a severe headache and becomes drowsy and feverish. The commonest cause would be an infection, that is meningitis. A less probable explanation would be bleeding into the brain from a burst blood vessel. Medical sciences can easily identify the particular cause in any one patient. With diseases causing loss of brain function, as with CJD, it is much harder to find the cause. So at present, we can be generally certain that CJD is caused by an infectious agent. That the disease sometimes runs in families is quite consistent with this: some families may have a particular predisposition to an infection; or else the infection could be passed from one generation to another, as is known to occur with Scrapie in sheep. Many infections are influenced by the genetic composition of the individual. For example, tuberculosis is more common in Asians than in Caucasians, although both are living in the same country.

One exceedingly unlikely proposition must be considered before it is dismissed—that is that the infectious agent CJD actually arises afresh within each person who is infected. This effectively suggests that infective agents spontaneously generate themselves. We know from the study of BSE in cattle that the infectious agent is acquired from the food; it does not generate itself in each animal that is infected. Studies of other infectious agents suggest that their formation may take millions or thousands of years, although once formed they can alter much more readily. This does argue very much against the formation from nothing of a similar agent in many people over such a short interval.

Therefore, we must consider CJD an infection, and this raises two questions: how was it acquired—that is, how did the infectious agent get into the person? And what is the source of the agent—that is, was it from another person, animal, soil, air or what?

To try and answer the first question, the actual routes by which infections get into the human body are well known. They are by direct contact with skin, through moist areas such as the eyes, through injections, through inhalation, through eating (i.e. ingestion), sexually, or from the mother to the baby. It is not possible to exclude any of these routes completely for CJD, but the two routes established for Scrapie in sheep are through ingesting and from ewe to lamb. Similarly, BSE in cattle is acquired by ingestion. It is believed that in these and other mammals the infectious agent resides inside the animal's cells and does not get into secretions such as milk. This means that routes such as inhalation, direct contact or through the eyes are exceedingly unlikely. The cases of CJD cannot be accounted by sexual contact, so ingestion does seem to be the only plausible route—at least for most of the patients infected.

In considering the source of the agent, the most significant information is that all the agents causing spongiform encephalopathies have been found in mammals, and in no other species. Kuru was transmitted by cannibalism in the Fore tribe, but this activity does not apply to CJD. Since the infectious agent is inside cells, and not in secretions, one would not expect it to be transferred between people by saliva. The human population seems an exceedingly unlikely source of the infectious agent for CJD.

Because the way that the infection is likely to enter the body is through ingestion, contact with cats, dogs or other domestic animals seems a most unlikely general explanation. Rather, we should study the possible food animals as the source. Worldwide, meat from only three mammals is eaten regularly—from sheep, pigs and cattle. Because Scrapie has been identified in sheep for many years, several studies have tried to see if there is any link between sheep Scrapie and human CJD. Three lines of evidence deny such a link. First, the incidence of Scrapie in sheep in the world varies widely from one country to another and there is little apparent association between the prevalence of Scrapie and that of CJD. Secondly, a careful American study by Carleton Gajdusek and his colleagues showed that patients with CJD had not eaten more sheep products than expected. Thirdly, in some countries, sheep's brains are considered a delicacy, and if the brain was from a Scrapie-infected animal it would be expected to contain a large amount of that infectious agent. There is no evidence of high prevalence of CJD in this population. The absence of evidence linking sheep Scrapie with CJD was reviewed by the Southwood and Tyrrell committees that advised the government. Both committees considered that there was no reason to believe that CJD was contracted from Scrapie-infected sheep.

During the latter part of 1989 and early in 1990, this absence of an association between sheep Scrapie and CJD was being used by MAFF and the Department of Health as evidence that BSE was not a hazard to man. The argument, presented to the public and the media, went as follows:

1 Scrapie has been prevalent in sheep for 200 years.
2 Scrapie does not infect man.

3   BSE in cattle was caused by the Scrapie agent from sheep.

4   Therefore BSE presents no danger to man.

The first two claims are essentially correct, as we have just seen; but we shall soon be looking at the lack of validity of claim 3, and in particular claim 4 will be shown to be untenable.

The point here is that the attempt to reassure us, by stating that CJD has not been contracted from sheep, has exactly the opposite effect. This is because it raises the question, 'If Scrapie is not the source of CJD, what is?' Pig meat might be, but as with sheep, there are three pieces of evidence against, and none in favour of this source. First, pig meat, usually as bacon or pork or ham, is obtained after slaughter of young animals—typically aged five to six months. At this age, any agent causing spongiform encephalopathy would be expected to be present in exceedingly low amounts. Secondly, there is no report to my knowledge of a spongiform encephalopathy occurring naturally in pigs; and thirdly, as mentioned earlier, the incidence of CJD is highest in Libyan Jews living in Israel—a community not expected to eat pig products. That BSE can experimentally pass to pigs by brain injection does not make a pig source for this disease likely; it does, however, show that the agent causing BSE has a host range probably including pigs. Pig tissues are very comparable to those of man.

So, by process of exclusion, beef products must be considered a possible source of the infectious agent for CJD. One reason for suspicion is that, of the food animals we eat regularly, the cow is the oldest, so the most likely to harbour large amounts of any such infectious agent, were it to be present. Beef cattle, and cows at the end of their useful milk production, are slaughtered when typically between three and ten years old. Apparently no research has been performed looking at the association of beef consumption and CJD, but it must be done urgently. For this hypothesis to be correct, it requires the presence of the infectious agent, if not the actual disease, in cattle twenty years or so ago. Consistent with this are the claims that a BSE-like illness has occurred previously in cattle in this country, or indeed in other countries. These claims have been made by, for example, spokespeople for the Meat and Livestock Commission, with the intention of reassuring the public that BSE is not new; we have had it around for years, it is all over the world, therefore there is no need for concern!

Unfortunately, the combination of the lack of evidence incriminating Scrapie in CJD, and the possibility that a low level of BSE has been prevalent for many years, raises frightening possibilities. The worst prediction for humans assumes that CJD was caused by the infectious agent in cattle many years ago. As a result of amplification of the numbers of this agent and through the rendering plant and feed, the future number of CJD cases could be multiplied many times over the current 1,500–9,000 cases. The horror of this possibility is presumably why the government's advisers hope that sheep Scrapie was the source of the cattle infection. The only real data presented to support this latter claim showed that the number of sheep reared has increased somewhat in recent years. However, no explanation has been offered as to why sheep Scrapie did not transfer to cattle before, since traditionally sheep and cattle have been reared on the same pasture and there is no reason to doubt that many cows would have eaten Scrapie-infected sheep material.

Apparently experiments have not been performed to see whether the Scrapie agent can be transferred from sheep to cows. or, if they have been performed, the results have not been published.

However, the exact source or sources of the agent causing BSE may not be that crucial in the creation of risk to humans. The important question is whether the agent is infectious for humans *after* it has multiplied in the cow. To make this point again, the Scrapie agent obtained directly from sheep has a capacity to infect different hosts from the agent obtained from mink (the disease to mink is abbreviated TME) *after* being acquired from sheep.

Agent	Scrapie from sheep	TME from mink
Infectious for Rhesus monkeys	-	+
Mice	+	-
Guinea pigs	-	+

It follows from this that even if it is assumed that Scrapie did transfer to bovines as BSE, and the Scrapie agent in sheep was not infectious to humans, we cannot be confident that the BSE agent from cattle will still not be infectious for us.

Beef Meat as a Potential Hazard to Humans
I have already considered the possibility of danger to people from cattle brain and other offal material incorporated into processed items. There is little reason to believe that the agents responsible for these types of disease are found actually within or around muscle fibres, although occasionally the agent has been transferred to animals from muscle after laboratory inoculation. However, the main danger from beef meat products is due to the presence of additional material, including:

1　Nerves that may contain infectious agent.
2　Lymphatics in channels and nodes around beef tissues that might be infectious.
3　the contamination of the carcass with spinal cords, brains and other 'high risk' tissues during the processing. In particular, the use of mechanical saws to remove bone could be hazardous in this way.

So far, in discussing the possible effect on humans, I have taken the most pessimistic view. Any one of the following could substantially reduce the risk.

The BSE could fail to gain access to the inside of the human body. It might not adhere to mucous membranes or be able to penetrate through the intestines; it might also be inactivated by blood or enzymes in the gut (although this is unlikely). If the BSE agent was variable in its properties, then at least some of these factors could reduce the risk of entry to the body. The agent might not survive or multiply in the cells of the body, or it might multiply so slowly that its adverse effects would not be manifested within the human lifespan.

The idea that an infective dose is required may not truly apply to the potential of the BSE agent to infect humans. It is not known why a certain number of infectious particles of these agents are generally required to induce experimental infections. The crucial question remains unanswered: Are many infectious particles required to provide the certainty of the infectious agent entering a particular body cell? If this were the case, then eating small amounts of agent on numerous occasions could provide the same risk as eating the total number of particles on just one occasion.

The more optimistic explanation is that immune mechanisms may satisfactorily eliminate the agent up to a critical number at any one time. Beyond that number, the agent 'wins the battle' and survives, then multiplies. If this were the case, the repetitive consumption of small numbers of particles over a long term should provide little infectious risk. Exceptions would be people with impaired immunity. With either explanation, pregnant women might be most vulnerable.

In conclusion, the scale of the BSE outbreak in the British Isles presents problems of unprecedented proportions. Whilst the evidence that the feed is responsible is compelling, the source of infection in the feed is not known, and the host range of BSE is not defined. Generally, infectious agents of the BSE type are capable of transfer experimentally to about half of the mammals tested. The recent description of the experimental transmission of the agent causing BSE from a cattle source to a pig suggests that the chances of spread to man may be somewhat more than 50 per cent. Pig tissues are well known to resemble those of humans. Because it is not possible to identify which British herds are free of the BSE agent, the advice must stand that British beef poses a risk and should be avoided. The danger is greatest in young children and pregnant women on account of the anticipated long incubation period of a BSE-like illness in man.

TABLE 9

Spongiform encephalopathies have occurred 'naturally' in the following mammals

Humans
Sheep (Scrapie)
Cattle (BSE)
Cats
Mink (TME)
Deer

TABLE 10

Features of BSE

Scale of epidemic unique to British Isles. Cows affected with clinical disease more often than cattle.

Most prevalent in S.W. and S. England.

Not known whether vertical transmission occurs to calves.

Not known whether humans are vulnerable.

The distribution of infectious agent is not known.

Rendering plants/protein supplements responsible.

Source of infectious agent possibly cattle.

Beef could be infectious for humans.

Uncertainties over infectivity to humans may persist for many years.

Cats have probably acquired the disease from cattle products.

More positive action required; it may be forced by economic pressures.

PART II

THE PROBLEMS OF FOOD PROCESSING, RETAILING AND COOKING

7 Food Processing— the Problems of Cook-Chill

Many—perhaps even the majority—of the foods consumed today have been subjected to processing. This means some type of treatment, conversion or mincing in factories at a stage in the food chain between the production of the whole raw food and its sale to the consumer. Food processing can be beneficial, in that with suitable heat treatment or other procedures, unwanted contaminants can be removed. However, it can also magnify the risk of food contamination by increasing the complexity of the final item; the addition of each new ingredient provides an opportunity to introduce contaminants.

Perhaps the greatest concern with food processing is the handling—notably storage times and temperatures—of the product after its release from the factory.

Some methods of processing and storing food have been well researched, have been in use for many years, and should be deemed safe—at least as safe as anything. Dry products such as breakfast cereals and crisps, deep-frozen items, or canned products, should cause few safety problems. However, the fashion for putting food heated by the canning process into flimsy containers may not be satisfactory because of possible punctures of the carton. At present this is being used increasingly with pet food and some convenience meals.

The products of most concern are those which have not been heated to high enough temperatures to kill all the bacteria, and are then stored under cool or chilled conditions which do not reliably prevent growth of certain bacteria. The deep-freeze temperature of -18°C to -23°C stops the growth of all bacteria. The chilled temperatures of say +5°C to +8°C certainly do not.

There is still some confusion over identifying the type of treatment any processed item has received. The convenience meals are an important example.

Some packeted convenience meals will be on sale at room temperature. There may be instructions for microwave reheating, in which case the container inside the decorated box will probably be plastic. The expiry or 'best by' date could be some months into the future. They may be described as 'long-life' or ambient temperature products. These have been prepared by a process similar to that used in canning, and all the bacteria and viruses should have been destroyed. As long as the packet is unpunctured and not bulging, they should be safe, although many people don't like their taste, the sauce seeming to grab the flavour from the major components, often poultry or fish.

The deep-frozen meals have been prepared with a system developed primarily for safe storage rather than as an intent to kill bacteria. After preparation in the factory, the individual meals are rapidly frozen and then stored under deep-frozen conditions, so that residual bacteria should have no chance of multiplying; the product on reheating should be almost as safe as when first made. Such deep-frozen items are stored in standing cabinets (preferably lidded) or sometimes in closed cupboards. Many of these deep-freezers do go through thaw cycles and the products' packaging may not feel as cold as you would expect. However, some products in the store should have visible ice crystals.

The chilled meals go through a preparation and first cooking procedure similar to that of the food that later is to be frozen. After decanting into individual receptacles, the temperature of the chilled meals is rapidly lowered to about 3°C and then stored/transported/stored before reaching the supermarket shelves, usually two to four days later. Although the temperature of the cold air in these open shelves may be near 0°C (thermometers will usually be at the back where the air is coldest, but this gives a false impression of the depth of the refrigerating effect), the actual food temperature could be between +5°C and +10°C. These are the worrying items.

Cook-Chill: Unsatisfactory Food Processing

The phrase 'cook-chill' has become familiar to most people only in the last few years; it will not be found in most modern dictionaries. One reason for this is that it does not have a precise identity. However, all such systems involve initial cooking of food at a site distant from where it will be eaten, followed by storage and transport under refrigerated temperatures, with reheating (often described for no sensible reason as regeneration) near to or at its serving. Some cooked and chilled products are consumed without being reheated but should also be considered within the general ambit of cook-chill.

There are two main views as to the reasons for the development of cook-chill: one from development of the use of cook-freeze; the other from the avoidance of waste of left-overs in the home, institutions or in catering. In the past, re-use of left-overs was never thought to enhance quality. One of the amazing aspects of cook-chill has been claims that the quality of food is actually improved by the technique.

Thus cook-chill food production did not develop in an organised way and was not adequately researched before its introduction. Instead it has evolved, generating its own momentum, from financial interests of equipment and food processing companies and by its capacity to satisfy two contemporary demands—the requirement for competitive tendering in institutional catering and the need for instantly available meals by some members of our society who are reluctant to prepare and cook their own food. The introduction of cook-chill is linked to the availability of refrigeration and hence its support in the past by the Electricity Council. However, the purpose of refrigerators had been primarily to avoid waste; never was it claimed that food would be improved by storing and then reheating. During the late 1960s, most catering systems that separated production and consumption of food employed an interval of holding under deep-freeze conditions. The margin of safety between the temperature of -18°C to -23°C and that of the lowest temperature at which moulds or bacteria can grow—that is, -10°C and -5°C respectively—was thought to be required to restrain the growth of these organisms under operational conditions. However, cook-freeze catering is relatively costly on electricity, and there can be problems of assembly of meals onto plates because the items tend to stick together. During the late 1960s cook-chill systems were being introduced in some countries, including the United States, France and Sweden. However, in the United Kingdom at this time concern over food safety resulted —commendably—in the publication in 1970 of the DHSS guidelines on cook-freeze catering.

These guidelines stated that cook-chill was not a suitable procedure for feeding a community on account of the risk of bacterial contamination. This document was produced after wide consultation with many experts, including medical doctors. However, during the 1970s the popularity of eating out in restaurants, the convenience of take-away food, and the need to feed passengers hot food while flying, often required meals to be prepared in advance, stored, chilled and then reheated when required. Many members of the public were then, and still are, unaware of this, seemingly reluctant to question the history of such food. This type of food was also beginning to appear in retail outlets—initially in the basements of a reputable chain of clothiers!

In 1980, the then DHSS published its guidelines for the safe operation of cook-chill. This presented a basic assumption that the system was inherently safe. Interestingly, this document only acknowledged two advisers, neither of whom was a medical microbiologist. The document in places resembled the advertising literature of one company selling the equipment required for the operation of the system. Essentially, it stated that the days of production and of consumption of the food should not be separated by more than three clear days of cold-holding at temperatures of between $0^{\circ}C$ to $+3^{\circ}C$, and that reheating should be performed at the place of consumption, which would seem to suggest, for example, in hospital wards rather than in the central kitchens. Oddly, during the last few years, with extension of this type of food into many supermarkets, not one of the 50 or more shops that I and my colleagues have visited complies with these guidelines as regards either the length of cold storage or the control of temperature (see below).

The 1980 DHSS guidelines totally failed to mention psychrotrophs: these are the bacteria able to cause spoilage of food or food poisoning after growth at low temperatures, and include listeria.

Bacteria That Can Cause Illness

Traditionally, the refrigeration of food has fulfilled two functions: first, to stop the growth of food spoilage bacteria and fungi, and secondly, to prevent growth and/or toxin formation by certain dangerous bacteria. Unfortunately, it is now known that at least five bacteria are able to grow at $5^{\circ}C$ or less and cause illness after being eaten. However, these bacteria do tend to grow more slowly at refrigeration temperatures of say, $3^{\circ}C-4^{\circ}C$ although at $8^{\circ}C-10^{\circ}C$, unfortunately the actual temperatures of many refrigerators, they grow more quickly.

The following are the bacteria able to grow under refrigeration, which can also cause harm:

1 *Listeria monocytogenes*. This will be described in Chapter 8.

2 *Clostridium botulinum* type E. Botulism is a severe, sometimes fatal, paralytic disease caused by the presence in contaminated food of a toxin produced by *Clostridium botulinum*. There are seven different types of these bacteria and toxins. Most human cases are caused by *C. botulinum* types A, B and E. An outbreak of type E botulism in the early 1960s, which was traced to vacuum-packed smoked fish, prompted studies into the ability of *C. botulinum* to grow at low temperatures. Only type E was found to grow at very low temperatures in beef stew. The bacteria could grow and produce toxin at temperatures as low as 3.3^0C. It is important to realise that irradiation of foods may allow more rapid toxin production at low temperatures, since harmless bacteria in the food are destroyed, yet spores of the *C. botulinum* survive and germinate (see Chapter 5).

Of particular concern is the *sous vide* variant of cook-chill catering. This creates an oxygen-free atmosphere in the package, which not only retards the growth of several competing micro-organisms (for example, pseudomonads) but also allows optimal growth of the dangerous clostridia.

In *sous vide* (which is French for 'under a vacuum'), meals or components of meals are first cooked in more or less the usual way. The final temperature is around 70^0C, so the food is certainly not overcooked. The food is then chilled and put into a pack from which air is excluded. This first cooking will not destroy the spores of *Clostridium botulinum*. The meals are kept refrigerated for anything up to six weeks. They may be found in restaurants, public houses, hotels and supermarkets, for the restaurateur sees them as a means of providing a wide variety of instantly available meals of satisfactory quality. So, on going to a restaurant with a very comprehensive menu and a short waiting time, the customer could be served with one of these products. They may be imported from France or other countries, and there are no laws in this country to control the length of storage time.

The danger could come if the storage temperature were greater than 3.3⁰C, which is certainly possible in practice. This would permit the spores of *Clostridium botulinum* type E to convert to the growing form and produce toxin.

The final reheating can be performed briefly by immersion of the pack in boiling water or by heating in a microwave, and may not destroy any toxin that had been produced. The system has not been adequately researched, and is another example of how our government's attitude permits the introduction of experimental food production methods without adequate testing for safety or monitoring controls.

So far as is known, the number of outlets with this type of product are still fairly small, and no illness has so far been reported after eating the product. It is clearly a case of 'an accident waiting to happen'.

3 *Yersina enterocolitica*. This bacterium is widely found in nature, and several types cause a range of intestinal infections in human beings. Those in children may mimic appendicitis—indeed, some normal appendices have been removed unnecessarily in consequence! It can sometimes get from the intestine to the blood; if it does, there is an associated mortality of 50 per cent in patients who are already ill. In 1978, an outbreak of this disease resulted from the consumption of contaminated chocolate milk that had been kept refrigerated.

The bacterium grows at temperatures as low as 1⁰C.

4 *Escherichia coli*. This is one of the commonest bacteria found in the normal human intestine. Several different types are responsible for a number of diseases, and some

produce toxins or poisons which are a common cause of travellers' diarrhoea. A few of these strains are capable not only of growth, but also of toxin production at 4°C. *E. coli* has certainly been isolated from cook-chill food.

5 *Aeromonas hydrophila.* Evidence is increasing that this bacterium, which is commonly found in fresh water, is an important cause of vomiting and diarrhoea, although some authorities remain unconvinced that it is really dangerous. The uncertainty seems to arise because not all strains are capable of causing disease. Contaminated foodstuffs may be a source of infection, and indeed the organism is found in refrigerated animal products. The growth of this bacterium can occur at temperatures as low as -0.1°C.

Where *Aeromonas hydrophila* is associated with disease, the patient is usually a child or an elderly person; the symptoms are mainly of severe diarrhoea, and the bacterium is found in large numbers in the intestine.

Development of Cook-Chill During the 1980s

After the publication of the Department of Health and Social Security's 1980 guidelines, the retail sector invested heavily in cook-chill production plant, distribution and retail facilities. The explosive commercial growth in this sector began in 1984, and the volume of sales is now worth about £200,000,000 annually. The middle 1980s also saw the development of cook-chill catering in institutions, notably in the NHS, the principal reason being apparently that it enabled the service to be put out for competitive tendering, with either the threat or actuality of privatisation. There is no doubt that the Department of Health was recommending this system to managers and was identifying by name food consultants who would support that recommendation. An extract of a paper submitted to Wakefield Health Authority in February 1986 is shown in Table 12 (p. 139). The claims made here in favour of cook-chill are truly remarkable when it is appreciated that the food was to be reheated in the existing kitchens—including that at Stanley Royd hospital—before distribution, warm, to the remote wards. Opposition to this scheme received publicity , correctly, in 1987 after nearly a million pounds of money had been spent on the production kitchen. Incidentally, virtually no consultation between management and staff occurred before this commitment. The details of this dispute will be considered later in this chapter.

In the light of our knowledge of the various bacteria that can grow at low temperatures, readers might like to consider these three simple proposed premises before the introduction of a catering system to feed a community.

1 The system should be able to restrain the growth or reappearance of all food poisoning bacteria.
2 There should be a margin of safety to allow for inevitable defects in equipment and temperature gauges and for human error.
3 There should be proper evaluation of the system before its introduction.

Cook-chill catering fails on all three counts. It is interesting that new guidelines released by the Department of Health on 22 June, 1989, after two years of agonising debate, state that the reheating of cook-chill food is required to ensure safety as well as palatability. This is a new and disturbing dimension to the problem since, previously, reheating has been used exclusively to confer palatability. In order to achieve this safety, the central food temperatures should be elevated to 70°C for two minutes. How can this stipulation be achieved in practice? Consider a reheating oven with thirty plated meals; there is likely to be one temperature check, possibly from one probe into one item of food. Suppose that temperature did show 70°C for two minutes, could we be quite confident that all the other food items were also heated correctly? The answer is no, since heat in ovens is never uniform. So the only procedure to use to be certain that this condition was met would be to insert a probe into every food item and to chart each one, so that each was shown to be over 70°C for two minutes. This is evident nonsense. So, once we have to rely on the reheating for microbial safety, then the problems mount. *Ovens for reheating have been designed primarily to achieve palatability, not safety.*

These second 1989 guidelines on cook-chill catering by the Department of Health are therefore an attempt to make the inherently unsafe system safe by the recommendation of the use of theoretical criteria that cannot be met in practice. One effect for those institutions already operating cook-chill operations is that the general reheating temperatures may have to be raised to 80°C to ensure that every item is heated to 70°C for two minutes. The resultant quality and nutritional content of the food may both be poor. Cynics argue that such food for consumption is either burnt or dangerous.

Retail Outlets
If the 1989 Department of Health guidelines, now being imposed on NHS hospitals, were indeed followed to the letter, does the retail sector comply? The answer is an emphatic no.

The Department of Health guidelines for the safe operation for the supply of cook-chill food are contravened in the retail sector in four ways.

1 The length of time of cold-holding is exceeded (see below).
2 The control of refrigeration is not adequate. This is most evidently seen on the supermarket shelves. Here, the products may be bathed in cold air at temperatures of 0°C–5°C; the fact that the shelves are open on one side and the products exposed to radiant heat from lighting

and other hot bodies, means that the actual temperature of the surface of the food is often higher—typically 5°C– 10°C.

3 Many of these cooked and chilled items are described as ready to eat hot or *cold*.

4 If such items are reheated, how can the consumer be certain that the central temperature has been raised to 70°C for two minutes whether heated in a conventional or microwave oven?

The procedures for the retail supply of cook-chill seem to be condoned by the Richmond Committee. The committee was set up in 1989 by the government in response to media concern over food safety. Some of the findings are commendable, but it failed to address the major commercial interests in cook-chill. The chairman was Professor Sir Mark Richmond, an eminent non-medical microbiologist, but membership of the committee was dominated by those working for the food industry. In Part I of this report, *The Microbiological Safety of Food (1990)*, discussion of such products includes the following statement: 'Safety is further assured by packaging into containers that protect the products from contamination and storage at temperatures of between 3°C and 7°C for typically between 6 and 10 days.'

There is therefore a very major discrepancy between two different advisory documents, published by the government in 1989 and 1990, involving temperature and time of holding of these products, and also their reheating. Both documents hope that bacteria which do not form spores are eliminated in the first heating process. This may, however, not always be achieved in practice. Moreover, recovery of heat-damaged bacteria might occur, as can post-cooking contamination. It is for these reasons that the more stringent Department of Health guidelines require a maximum cold holding temperature of 3°C and up to only three days between the day of first cooking and the day of reheating. Richmond condones 7°C and ten days.

The Department of Health's document requires reheating to elevate the centre temperature of each food item to at least 70°C for two minutes, and so apparently excludes all items that are to be consumed without reheating. The Richmond approach hardly considers reheating and certainly does not state that this procedure is required to confer safety.

With our knowledge of the nature of psychrotrophic bacteria, notably their resistance to heat, we must prefer the stipulations proposed by the Department of Health, rather than those of Richmond. It appears as if the proposals of the latter are saying (in effect): with the present organisation of these systems in the retail sector, it is impossible for them to comply with the stipulations of the Department of Health—hence their own operational details have to be accepted!

This surely is the incorrect approach. Should not the whole operation have been carefully researched, particularly at the point of consumption? Following this, precise controls on the system should have been imposed.

Nutrition of Cook-Chill Foods

The nutritional content of meals eaten occasionally may not be important so long as the rest of the diet can compensate for any deficiencies. However, if a catering system provides the exclusive source of nourishment for people or patients in an institution, then its nutritional content must be adequate. That there may be a need to supplement cook-chill food with vitamins, etc., does suggest concern over the presence of certain nutrients. Because no study has been published assessing the nutrients of the entire cook-chill system relative to other systems used to feed a community, it is only possible to point to concerns rather than to certainties.

The first relates to the amount of polyunsaturated fatty acids. I myself subscribe to the view that polyunsaturated fatty acids are desirable—some are even essential—for a number of body functions, as part of the structure of cells, stopping our arteries 'furring up' and for the making of some hormones. Unfortunately such fatty acids fare badly in cook-chill operations, with a tendency to decompose under cold storage, resulting not only in loss of active compound, but also in the formation of some unpleasant-smelling products. Thus food such as fish, and many vegetables thought generally to be desirable for nutrition, are not at all easy to process by the cook-chill system. It seems extraordinary that, having identified the desirability of polyunsaturated fatty acids over many years, catering methods are being developed which knowingly reduce the amount of these substances. Other concerns include the B vitamins such as folic acid, and essential amino acids such as lysine, which may well be lost during this process.

Taste and Smell
This must be the most difficult aspect to investigate, but common sense must suggest that food produced by cook-chill methods is inferior generally to conventional catering. The last cook-chill meal offered to me was a dish consisting of chicken legs in a white sauce. The bones projected from the meat and were grey-black, the meat was dry and tasteless and the sauce was unpleasant, insipid and gelatinous. The vegetables were limp, soggy and tasteless. Claims that cook-chill improves quality are usually based on the fact that, in hospitals, reheating at ward level can result in hot food. If cook-chill food is, from the point of view of taste and smell, preferred to conventional food, then there must be something seriously amiss with the latter that can be improved.

Cost
No proper financial appraisal of the true costs of cook-chill has been published since the system came into operation in institutions. Many of the financial savings anticipated

before implementation will not be realised in practice. Costs such as increased requirement for energy, the cost of maintenance and replacement of the expensive equipment, and the cost of monitoring, may come as unpleasant surprises. Furthermore, because of the indifferent quality of the food, the system requires to be supplemented with other food, including frozen diets for selected patients. These meals have to join the cook-chill system after thawing, and their resultant quality can be expected to be poor. Many staff canteens now supplement their cook-chill operation with salads, chips cooked on the spot and omelettes and sandwiches. Extra staff are required for these. Generally, the reheating of meals at ward level will also require extra catering staff. Indeed, many of the reheating costs seem to be ignored by certain catering 'consultants'.

Abuse of Cook-Chill

One of the problems of cook-chill catering is that because the system has not been adequately researched and is poorly defined, it is open to substantial abuse. The events in Yorkshire between 1984 and 1989 illustrate many of these problems. I shall present the details of this episode in full, mainly to show how it was first impressed on me that national attitudes were seriously amiss over food.

The story starts in 1983, when I went to Leeds as Professor of Medical Microbiology. This is a post which provides both university teaching and duties to the Health Service, including involvement with patients—preventing, identifying and treating infections. The department has a wide range of research interests, including food microbiology. The overriding commitment would seem to be the welfare of patients. Elsewhere in Yorkshire microbiology was then fairly poorly developed. There had been a lack of interest in the subject and some hospitals did not have their own expert, whether an NHS consultant or an academic to look after the interests of patients through diagnosis and treatment of infections. As a result, the department in Leeds was approached in the summer of 1984 to inquire whether it would offer consultant help to Wakefield Health Authority about twelve miles to the south; the response was yes. In late August, while the contracts were being formalised through the NHS bureaucracy, with the Regional Health Authority and the Department of Health having to ratify such an arrangement, a salmonella outbreak occurred in one of the Wakefield hospitals (Stanley Royd). The department in Leeds was not consulted, because the bureaucratic procedures had not been completed. So the most appalling events taking place were just watched; appalling not so much because of concern about what was in effect a single-point food poisoning outbreak, but concern from speculation and amplification by the media.

It so happened that, earlier that same year, a much more serious salmonella outbreak had occurred, of which most of us remained ignorant as it received scant publicity—on British Airways planes going from Heathrow to the United States. Seven hundred and sixty-six people were involved, and two deaths, whereas at Stanley Royd there were 455 cases. The Heathrow outbreak was the first major epidemic with *Salmonella enteritidis*, the 'egg strain', and it was also the first major outbreak associated with food produced by a cook-chill production kitchen. Apparently the salmonella found its way into an aspic glaze for a fish item. The details have not been published.

In the absence of a local microbiologist, the Wakefield outbreak was managed with help from elsewhere. On 1 January, 1985, the department in Leeds formally took responsibility for microbiology in Wakefield, with the issue of food poisoning and its prevention as a major concern. During that year morale among staff in the Wakefield hospitals was low; any gastro-intestinal illness was immediately attributed to the hospital food—usually wrongly! Morale was particularly low during the public inquiry into the food poisoning outbreak of the previous year, which was held in the late spring and summer. The inquiry reported in January 1986: within a comprehensive document, the cause of the outbreak was attributed to catering errors in the Stanley Royd kitchens against a background of inadequate management. On 27 February, 1986, Wakefield Health Authority responded to this report and accepted the principal conclusions, including those requiring that there should be a short maximum interval of 24 hours between the cooking of food and its consumption. The following day, the Authority adopted a proposal from the management to introduce cook-chill catering, which does of course extend the time between cooking and eating to several days.

The decision at the Authority then, and subsequently, was not unanimous, four members being implacably opposed. The main reason for the cook-chill proposal was apparently to save £300,000 per annum. The medical, nursing and catering staff had not been consulted beforehand, nor had the microbiologists. The unit to produce the food—that is, cooking, chilling and storing—was to be a converted conventional kitchen, and the reheating and distribution were to utilise the existing facilities —including those associated with the Stanley Royd salmonella problem.

However, these plans were to remain unknown to patients and staff until March 1987, a full year after the decision to proceed had been taken. Although the new kitchen was near completion at this time, it was publicity over the refusal of catering staff to operate the intended scheme 'on grounds of hygiene' that brought the issue into public scrutiny for the first time.

When members of our department in Leeds were made aware of the scheme, they were appalled for three reasons.

First, there had been concern over the safety of cook-chill operations for many years, so much so that the then Department of Health and Social Security issued a warning in 1970 that cook-chill catering was not a safe method of feeding a community on account of the risk of bacterial contamination.

Secondly, the proposal at Wakefield was to save money by employing existing reheating and distribution methods which were patently unsatisfactory.

Thirdly, neither members of the department nor any medical or nursing staff had been consulted. The reason for this omission has never been explained.

In April 1987, officers of Wakefield Health Authority convened a meeting to discuss how to proceed with their cook-chill catering. It was clear that the proposal as it stood, to reheat food in the existing kitchens followed by a transport time of up to two hours, would produce food of low nutrition and possible dangers. The gist of this appeared in unconfirmed minutes sent to members of the Authority. One member 'leaked' this document to the *Yorkshire Post* which with alacrity carried a story including a statement that the proposed food was 'microbiologically unsound and nutritionally unsafe'.

In June 1987, the Yorkshire Regional Health Authority made a great deal of publicity about the setting up of an expert group whose terms of reference were: 'To review and advise the RHA on the safe implementation and subsequent safe operation of cook-chill systems in the Region with special reference to the monitoring arrangements, quality control procedures and their management, having regard to good practice and the guidelines issued by the DHSS in 1980.'

The group contained no medical microbiologist. The report appeared at the end of September 1987 with a blaze of publicity, and made the comment that the proposals for Wakefield were satisfactory so long as the time between reheating and serving was less than 15 minutes. The members of the expert group had visited Wakefield, and it is incredible that they were not aware that this time stipulation could not possibly be complied with in practice.

During that autumn the reality of this became clear to everyone at Wakefield, including the general manager, Mr Brian Birchall, and the then Chairman of the Health Authority, Sir Jack Smart, who had the responsibility of evaluating proposals from the general manager. The transfer of reheating of the chilled food from the central kitchens, with their operational distribution network, to each ward, would require substantial extra investment. The Chairman and some members of the Health Authority now saw cook-chill catering as a procedure that would actually require extra funds rather than save any. In addition, the problems of possible poor quality of food and the safety issues were not resolved. During the winter and spring of 1988 a series of meetings of the Health Authority argued these issues at length. Public confrontation between Mr Birchall and Sir Jack Smart led to the Regional Health Authority setting up an inquiry into the affairs of the Wakefield Health Authority. The outcome—predictable to many observers—was to blame Sir Jack Smart for much of the *impasse* and he was subsequently dismissed from his post. The Regional Health Authority found the £350,000 needed to pay for the reheating equipment at ward level for cook-chill from a special 'contingency' fund, and the new Chairman of Wakefield Health Authority was Mr Brian Hayward, who had been Chairman of the Regional Health Authority's 'expert' group.

At the time of writing, numerous complaints have been raised about the quality of the cook-chill food, about a million pounds has been spent on the introduction of this catering and the anticipated shortfall for the District for 1989–90 is approaching one million pounds (B. Birchall, *Yorkshire Post*, 2 November, 1989).

Flushed with their success at Wakefield, the Yorkshire Regional Health Authority's catering group, under the Chairmanship of Mr Brian Birchall, proposed in the summer of 1988 to introduce cook-chill catering into all 128 hospitals in Yorkshire. As a prelude to this, each district was asked to comment on the proposal, the essence of which was that *independent* consultants had said it was the ideal option, a great deal of money would be saved, and the system was perfectly safe. No details were given, and many districts raised serious objections, notably Leeds Western. Members of this Health Authority were of the view that, for some inexplicable motive, the decision had in reality been taken before the option appraisal.

In the autumn of 1988 the Regional Health Authority stated its intention to proceed with cook-chill catering in all the hospitals, and publicly stated it had the support of all the health districts.

By the summer of 1990, the scheme had apparently been quietly dropped.

In summary, cook-chill provides the facility to process composite moist food items, and to provide their ready availability to the public. Because there are no problems of food components adhering to each other as occurs in cook-freeze systems, cook-chill's versatility is seen as an important manufacturing process. Unfortunately, the investment into it was largely made before the significance of listeria and other psychrotrophs was appreciated. Indeed, the process has still not been adequately researched. A suspicion remains that the food processor considers that his responsibility is discharged on the dispatch of the food from the factory. However, by the time the food is consumed it could well be dangerously contaminated. Virtually none of the commercial/retail cook-chill systems comply with the recent directives concerning safety from the Department of Health. They do in the main, as expected, operate within the recommendations from the Ministry of Agriculture.

The failure of the government to put adequate controls over commercial cook-chill operations is a clear example of its concern for the food producers rather than the consumers. The advice to the consumer is simple. Do not buy these products.

TABLE 11

Types of convenience meals

1 Deep frozen meals. These should be almost as safe as when first frozen. Reheat to palatable temperatures.

2 Ambient temperature meals. Should be effectively sterile, having been subjected to the 'canning' process. May last for months. Safe, if rather boring in flavour.

3 Cook-chill meals in the retail sector. Unsafe. Do not comply with recommendations of Department of Health. Best avoided.

TABLE 12

Extract from paper presented by the Wakefield management to Wakefield Health Authority, arguing for the introduction of cook-chill catering with reheating in existing kitchens. Paper dated 28 February, 1986

1 To improve the quality, variety and nutritional value of food.

2 To produce an environment and pattern of work flow which is conducive to high standards of hygiene.

3 To increase control of food production.

4 To centralise primary catering staff skills.

5 To improve the flexibility of catering services to meet future patterns of demand within the District.

6 To create a viable unit of business as recommended by the latest guidance issued by the DHSS in respect of competitive tendering.

7 To reduce operational costs.

8 Listeriosis

The disease listeriosis results from an infection by a bacterium called *Listeria monocytogenes*. The disease and bacteria owe their name to the famous nineteenth-century surgeon, Lord Lister, who pioneered antiseptic surgery.

Although since the 1920s and 1930s infection by listeria has been known to occur in both humans and some animals, the proof that food was the main route by which people became infected was not discovered until about 1982, when an outbreak in Eastern Canada was found to be due to coleslaw contaminated with listeria from vegetables including cabbage, radishes and carrots, fertilised with sheep manure. Unfortunately, by this time a major commitment had already been made in many countries to new food processing, distribution and storage methods, and it is now becoming clear that the bacterium *Listeria monocytogenes* may not be controlled by some procedures established for the control of other types of food poisoning.

Listeria are long straight rods which can actively swim in fluids at 20°C but not at 37°C. The bacteria are quite easy to grow in the laboratory and it should be possible for most doctors to diagnose human listeriosis so long as the possibility of the disease has been considered.

The Human Disease

Two major types of human listeriosis are recognised: these are referred to as the materno-fetal and adult-juvenile types. In materno-fetal listeriosis, a pregnant woman develops a characteristic 'flu-like' illness which may then lead, after a variable period of time, to abortion, delivery of a stillborn child, or the birth—often premature—of a child now suffering from listeriosis. The baby in the womb is infected as a result of passage of the bacteria across the placenta, having gained access to the mother's blood. Infants who develop listeriosis have very high mortality rates and there is a high incidence of brain damage in the survivors, such as hydrocephalus, mental handicap and blindness.

In adults, listeriosis may develop as a meningitis and sometimes as a blood-borne illness. Other forms of infection, such as those affecting the heart and eye, are uncommon. Despite the availability of antibiotics that should work in theory, the overall mortality rate for adult-juvenile listeriosis is 25-30 per cent.

Until fairly recently it was considered that listeriosis occurred only in certain individuals, the so-called vulnerable people: pregnant women, the very young, the elderly and patients with impaired immunity, such as those receiving transplants, individuals with cancer, or AIDS sufferers. However, it is now apparent that up to 30 per cent of cases of listeriosis occur in otherwise healthy individuals.

The Animal Disease
As with human listeriosis, the incidence of the disease in animals has recently increased. In several countries listeriosis in livestock, particularly sheep, is of considerable economic importance and has led to the development of listeria vaccines. The disease is most commonly seen in winter and early spring, unlike human illness where the peak incidence is seen during the summer.

The major effects of animal listeriosis are abortion or stillbirth, blood poisoning in unweaned animals and inflammation of the brain in adults. Animals can develop mastitis, which partly accounts for the result that some milk samples may contain listeria.

Of the various animals that have been infected, sheep and cattle are the most commonly afflicted, two of the distressing symptoms they suffer being blindness and a peculiar walking gait, sometimes in a circular fashion.

The Source of the Bacterium

Listeria bacteria are widely distributed in nature, being found in soil, sewage, river water, vegetable matter, silage, other animal fodder, insects, rarely in the human intestines, raw milk, and kitchen premises. They have been identified from all continents except Antarctica, and have been found in at least 37 species of animal and seventeen species of bird.

The main cause of listeriosis in animals is thought to be through silage, particularly in sheep. The disease results from listeria flourishing in the silage as a consequence of the acidity being lower than usual, owing to contamination by alkaline faeces, and by molehills; in addition, the use of large bales may be important. It is interesting that cold conditions and an acidity (or pH) of 5.0-5.5 provide the optimum conditions for production and activity of the bacterium's chief poison, or toxin. The disease is not common in poultry and exceedingly rare in pigs. The number of occasions when a direct animal-to-human transfer has been demonstrated are few indeed: occasionally veterinary surgeons have acquired infected cuts; one case of pneumonia in a Norwegian sheep farmer, and a few instances of infected eyes in poultry works have been described. It should be pointed out that even some of these reports are not well documented. In contrast, the number of cases indicating that food is the means of causing human infection approaches 1,000. Whilst it is true that over recent years the number of sheep and cattle suffering from listeriosis may have increased, there is no reason to blame the increase in human cases on this, especially since the reporting of animal cases is

notoriously incomplete and haphazard. The various ways
that listeria bacteria can be transferred in nature are shown
in Figure 1 below.

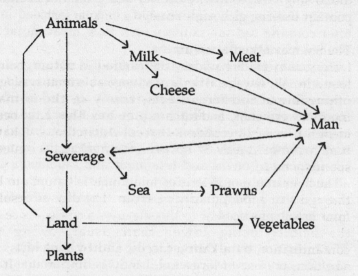

Figure 1.   *The listeria 'cycle'*

Listeria has been found in a variety of raw foods, usually
in rather small numbers: among vegetables about one to
ten per cent of samples, including lettuce, cabbage,
Brussels sprouts, broccoli, cauliflower, asparagus, carrots,
tomatoes and radishes. Listeria has also been found in
some salamis and in between two per cent and 50 per cent
of cook-chill products. Since the initial description from
Leeds University in 1988, of 25 per cent of cook-chill
products being contaminated, many other surveys have
confirmed this. The government-run Public Health
Laboratory Service found overall that twelve per cent of
the products were contaminated, and others who have
mainly published their findings in the national press have
found the lowest incidence (two per cent) in school and

hospital food just after production, with the highest incidence being in poultry after several days' cold storage. For example, Leeds Environmental Health Department found seven out of twelve cooked and chilled chickens to contain listeria, although roasted chicken sampled just after cooking did not contain any. Raw meat, notably poultry, may also contain listeria.

Thus many foods harbour listeria and it is not surprising that the World Health Organisation considered it impossible to eliminate the bacterium altogether from food. Nevertheless, listeria is not by any means the only cause of food-borne illness that is widely distributed in man, animals, and/or nature. *Staphylococcus aureus*, *Clostridium perfringens* and *botulinum*, and salmonella are all such examples and it is certainly possible to minimise the risks of food poisoning from them by adopting appropriate practices.

The Incidence of the Disease in the United Kingdom

The number of *reported* cases of listeriosis from laboratories has increased from around 20-30 annually twenty years ago, to 259 for 1987 and an estimated number of 300 or more from 1988. Since the publicity over the disease in 1989, the number of official reports has gratifyingly dropped considerably: the figures for 1990 are expected to be about 100. During this period 1968–1988, the procedures for identifying the bacteria from patients have altered little, nor have the reporting procedures changed. Listeria remains a 'non-notifiable' disease, so that laboratories and clinical doctors are under no legal obligation to notify cases. A considerable number, such as elderly patients at home or miscarriages in early pregnancy, will be missed. In the United States, where more action has been taken than in the United Kingdom, the estimated annual number of cases is 1,600 (counting mothers and infected babies as a single case), with 400-500 deaths (Broome, 1988). For the United Kingdom we have to ask by what factor the notified cases should be multiplied to achieve the actual incidence. With salmonella food poisoning, a multiplier of times ten is usually used; for listeriosis this is probably too high because the disease tends to be more serious than salmonella and fewer cases will be missed. Fairly accurate figures for listeriosis are known for some localities. We believe that the real incidence is about three-fold of the reported cases. The risk of dying (that is, the mortality) with listeriosis—even with antibiotic treatment—is about 25-30 per cent. This means that between 1968 and 1988 the number of deaths attributable to listeriosis rose to about 200 annually—or about double those due to salmonella food poisoning.

How Listeria Causes Disease
Although listeria is found in many raw foods and also in some processed food, only a tiny minority of people acquire the disease after eating contaminated food. The greatest unsolved problem concerning listeriosis is to account for the infrequency of actual infection—even in vulnerable groups—in the presence of a high frequency of contamination of certain foods. Little is known of exactly how listeria gets into the body, although the portal of entry for the organisms must be the gastrointestinal tract. It appears that *L. monocytogenes* can alter the surface of the intestinal mucosa and so permit its entry to the body. The first line of defence against invading micro-organisms is what are known as white cells or leucocytes, and these appear unable to destroy listeria as efficiently as they do some other organisms. This is because the listeria bacteria produce a toxin or poison that actually damages the cells; the bacteria therefore survive and multiply in these cells, and may even be carried to other parts of the body.

So far the ability of the listeria bacteria to gain access to the patient has been considered almost in isolation of the general behaviour of the bacterium. Humans are but one component in a cycle involving sewage, water, animals, plants, and food. We know that the numbers and types of bacteria in our intestines are influenced by our diet, and also by eating specific micro-organisms in our food. One of the anxieties expressed concerning the regular ingestion of food produced by the cook-chill method is that it could alter the numbers and types of bacteria resulting from ingestion of traditionally produced food. Because listeria is relatively resistant to heat, and can grow under cold conditions (down to 0^0C, although slowly) it will be expected to flourish in cook-chill types of food at the expense of other, harmless bacteria. Research is needed to see whether this type of food, eaten regularly, does in fact alter the nature of the bacteria in our intestines.

Infective Dose

The number of listeria bacteria required to initiate an infection in any individual is not known, and must be one of the many variables that contribute to disease. This problem is not capable of experiment in humans for obvious ethical reasons. If a patient develops listeriosis, it is probable that the food in question has been discarded by the time the illness is diagnosed, since the time between eating the food and the onset of the illness varies from several days to five weeks. A further time of one to three days is needed to diagnose the illness. So if any food is still available, it will be examined perhaps one to four weeks after it caused the disease and the number of bacteria will have changed, by an extremely uncertain amount, between those that cause the infection and those that were recovered later. However, where a large outbreak is 'ongoing', as occurred with Mexican cheese in California in 1985, some assessment may be made of the infective dose. The Mexican-style cheese implicated in the Californian outbreak contained about a hundred to a thousand *Listeria monocytogenes* per gramme of cheese.

In conclusion, *Listeria monocytogenes* is the bacterium, able to grown under cold conditions, which has been most studied. Many questions remained, notably the reason why some people become ill from it, whilst others do not. Food is the major source of the bacterium, and its two remarkable properties—resistance to heat and its ability to flourish under refrigeration temperatures—should have caused a major rethink by the food industry. There is still little evidence for this, and the onus is still with the consumer not to eat risky foods. This is not acceptable in the long term. The food industry should be required by law to use processes that ensure food is safe at the point of sale for all the population. Recent legislation has not addressed this issue.

9 Food Poisoning: How it Affects You

The effect that food poisoning has on people is not completely predictable, but is definitely unpleasant. The most dramatic symptoms are seen when food is eaten, in which bacteria have already produced toxins. Food poisoning can also include illness from chemicals or fungal toxins. Viruses and some bacteria such as listeria and campylobacter are not causes of food poisoning in the strictest sense: they are really food-borne infections. However, the micro-organisms that directly cause illness after being eaten comprise a practical group and will be considered here whether or not they cause classic poisoning.

The Host
Readers will be aware that certain individuals are more prone to suffer from the effects of food poisoning than others—for example, the elderly, pregnant women, newborn babies, those with particular diseases, those taking certain drugs and generally those whose immune systems are defective. This is true generally, but some apparently healthy people can sometimes suffer severe symptoms, even from infections due to listeria or salmonella. It is possible that some of these individuals possess immunological defects of which they are not aware. Moreover, to state that vulnerable people are more prone to food poisoning than healthy people is nothing more than a dishonest tautology that has been used by the government and its food industry to avoid the difficult issues of whether whole batches of food would be

withdrawn from availability. In practical terms, it is not possible to identify exactly who is vulnerable in advance of their symptoms. For example, the timing, and awareness, of pregnancy is never exact and a person's chronological age cannot be used to define whether he is vulnerable. Some people aged 70 are fitter and more resistant to diseases, such as food poisoning, than those ten years younger.

Salmonella Food Poisoning

This results from the survival of the eaten bacteria through the stomach acid and their subsequent growth in the intestine. In the great majority of cases the illness begins twelve to twenty-four hours after eating contaminated food, and almost always by 48 hours. The longer interval occurs in some people already ill, who may have eaten just a small number of bacteria, and in the elderly people in whom food can take a long time to pass through the intestinal tract. The symptoms result from the damage by the salmonella bacterium's poison (called an enterotoxin) on the lining of the intestine, so that absorption of water and salts is prevented. These cause fluid to collect in the inside of the intestines. Colicky abdominal pain, usually all over the abdomen, with urgent and explosive diarrhoea, are the first features. The temperature may be raised to 39°C, but not always. Vomiting can occur—we do not exactly know why, perhaps due to toxins getting into the blood. After some hours, loss of water and salts in the diarrhoea, associated with a feeling of disinclination to drink, cause signs and symptoms of dehydration—sunken eyes, dry mouth, loss of skin firmness, production of small amounts of concentrated urine and a rising pulse rate.

It is the combined loss of water and salts that is particularly dangerous. Loss of water alone results in an increase in concentration of salts in the blood, which causes a transfer of water from inside the body cells to the blood, so restoring the blood volume that is essential for life. Loss of water and salts together does not produce this transfer or osmotic pull; rather other, less effective mechanisms of blood volume control come into play. Elderly people may be particularly poor at compensating for loss of water and salts from the blood. If so, the blood volume shrinks, the pulse rate rises farther, and the blood pressure drops. The entire circulation can fail and complications of low blood pressure can occur, such as strokes and heart attacks. If death occurs from acute food poisoning—of any cause—these are what actually induce it.

Fortunately, most people begin to recover within a few days, with the diarrhoea becoming less, although blood and mucus may have been passed for a time. However, full return to health can take weeks and depends on the slow process of the correction of the losses of water and salts in the various parts or compartments of the body. During this period, the patient may experience considerable thirst and large amounts of urine may be passed. He or she may feel exhausted, or mentally and physically lethargic. This can last for a surprisingly long time, even for a month.

Whilst death is rare, and recovery usual, in about one to two per cent of patients bacteriological complications occur, particularly in those who are ill or elderly. These risks appear to be most associated with *S. enteritidis* and *S. typhimurium*, and result from the bacteria escaping from the inside of the intestine to the bloodstream. This occurs fairly soon after onset of symptoms—indeed, the diarrhoea may never be an important feature of the illness. When the salmonella multiplies in the blood, symptoms of general blood poisoning or septicaemia occur—that is, high fever (40–41°C), violent shivering or rigors, rapid pulse rate, low blood pressure, and wheezing. Admission to hospital and a correct treatment should usually lead to recovery. Appropriate antibiotics include chloramphenicol, trimethoprim, ciprofloxacin and, sometimes, ampicillin.

Blood poisoning of any cause may produce complications. For example, the bacteria can be instrumental in causing a bulging weakness known as an aneurysm of the major artery from the heart, to burst, or the infecting bacteria can be deposited in tissues and produce abscesses almost anywhere—for example in the bones, kidneys, brain or lungs. These are usually treatable, although they can be the 'last straw' in people with other severe illnesses. About 70-100 people die annually from salmonella infection in the United Kingdom.

Campylobacter Food Poisoning

Whilst the peak of annual incidence of salmonella infection occurs in August and September, that of campylobacter is in June and July. There is no obvious explanation for this. Another difference between these types of food poisoning is that there is reason to believe that people can develop immunity to campylobacter, but not to salmonella infection. Campylobacter infection occurs particularly in children and young adults, with the lower incidence in later life possibly resulting from immunity. The disease results from the sheer numbers of bacteria in the gut. Specimens of faeces from an ill patient viewed under the microscope may appear to be composed of almost solid campylobacter bacteria. These are typically small, comma- or seagull-shaped.

This explains why the number of bacteria needed to generate an illness, or infective dose, whilst being small, can produce illness some five to ten days after eating the food in question—that is the time needed for bacteria to multiply to enormous numbers to cause disease. The illness may develop gradually, with fever, listlessness and nausea. There is abdominal pain, colicky and sometimes remarkably severe. The diarrhoea is watery, explosive and frequently intermixed with mucus and blood. The symptoms abate over several days, although as with salmonella food poisoning, full recovery may take more than a week. Fatality is exceedingly rare, although complications can occur, such as perforation of the bowel which may require surgery. One of the problems with campylobacter infection is that the long incubation period may make the identity of the food source difficult to discover and the symptoms are similar to those of inflammatory bowel disease, such as ulcerative colitis or even cancer. Tests that reveal campylobacter to be the cause of the illness may come as a relief to both patient and doctor! However, these procedures take time, money and generate anxiety. The adverse effect of food poisoning due to campylobacter, numerically the most common type, on society is considerable. The bacteria are usually sensitive to antibiotics such as erythromycin and nalidixic acid, but there is little evidence that they are of benefit in practice, presumably because they are given too late. Spread of the infection from one person to another, such as mother to child, can occur but is not common.

The main cause of campylobacter food poisoning is thought to be under-cooked poultry, for example from barbecues or microwave ovens. Unpasteurised milk may also be a source, and even magpies have been blamed for contaminating milk on the doorstep.

The Nasty Toxins
Clostridium perfringens remains a puzzle: we do not know how it causes symptoms, since most normal individuals harbour the organism in their intestines, often in quite high numbers—for example, ten thousand per gramme of faeces. Perhaps, during its growth in warm food, more toxin is formed than in the intestines. The chief symptom is diarrhoea, typically twelve to eighteen hours after eating contaminated food. Passing of blood is not common. The other troublesome symptom is colicky abdominal pain. Vomiting is rare. The illness usually abates after two to three days. One of the diseases it can mimic is gastro-enteritis due to small round viruses such

as rotaviruses that can be acquired from food, and seemingly through air and touch.

Clostridium botulinum is still surprisingly rare as a food poisoning cause, despite the widespread distribution of its spores. The course of the disease is due to the absorption of the toxin intact and its deposition at the junctions between nerves and muscles. Typically, the disease proceeds as follows. About six to twelve hours (or possibly longer) after eating the contaminated food, nausea, vomiting and a dry mouth occur. This is followed by weakness and an inability to stand. Blurred and double vision result from paralysis of the muscles responsible for co-ordinating sight. Paralysis of other muscles causes inability to speak and swallow; by the time normal breathing is disrupted, the patient will hopefully have been admitted to hospital if he or she is to have a chance of survival. Botulism is, therefore, a rapidly developing disease involving likely paralysis of all motor muscles. In this way it is not unlike poliomyelitis. These illnesses are particularly dreadful because the sensory functions of nerves are not affected, so there is full awareness of the developing paralysis.

Treatment in hospital involves life-support for the paralysed patient, who will be sedated. Drugs to neutralise the toxin work, but only partly. Improvement is slow, with treatment aimed at maintaining all vital functions until spontaneous recovery of muscle function occurs. Once recovery has been made, it should be permanent. Up to about 1960, the mortality from botulism in the United States was about 60 per cent. It should be less now because of improvement in life-support techniques. It is interesting that cases of botulism throughout this century have always been more common in the United States than in the United Kingdom, and these differences cannot be explained by risks from defects in canning alone. In the future in the United Kingdom, there are fears that botulism could once more become a regular disaster on account of the expansion of *sous vide* catering (see Chapter 7).

Food poisoning from *Staphylococcus aureus* results from eating food containing poisons called enterotoxins released by some strains. This toxin is rapidly absorbed from the stomach and acts on the brain. The resultant vomiting occurs usually between 30 minutes and three hours after eating the poison and can be severe and bloodstained. The temperature may be subnormal, and the skin sweaty. The patient usually recovers over the next two days. The progression of the disease resembles that due to acute alcohol poisoning or to highly spiced food. All three may occur together, as with the midnight curry after a long binge!

Two types of food poisoning are caused by *Bacillus cereus*, a bacterium found very widely in the environment. The first type resembles that caused by *Clostridium perfringens*. The illness starts about twelve hours after eating contaminated food and the main symptoms are diarrhoea and abdominal pains for a day or so. In the second type, probably the most common food responsible is cooked rice. Typically, after two or three hours a feeling of nausea is followed by actual vomiting, which can be severe and last for up to a day. Diarrhoea is uncommon, but patients feel exhausted for several days afterwards. This type of illness seems to reflect modern eating habits, and fried rice from Chinese take-away restaurants is nearly always involved.

Vibrio parahaemolyticus is shaped like a small comma and has a long, whiplike tail that enables it to move rapidly in fluids. It can produce some poisons but is easily damaged by temperatures as low as 50°C held for a few minutes, and will not grow readily in food that is on the acid side. *Vibrio parahaemolyticus* is naturally found in the sea, often in shallow water, mud and estuaries, and flourishes in the summer, so it may be present in raw fish, prawns, crabs, lobsters and oysters. In Japan fish is often eaten raw, and food poisoning from this *Vibrio* is quite common. In Britain it is rare.

The disease starts between twelve and twenty-four hours after eating contaminated food. Colicky abdominal pain and diarrhoea occur. Many patients feel sweaty and suffer from headaches. Although these symptoms improve in two or three days, a feeling of tiredness can last longer.

Conclusion

The intention here is to highlight the distressing symptoms of some of the causes of food poisoning. However, many patients with food poisoning have mild but still troublesome systems, and do not consult their doctors. Many doctors do not make the diagnosis or notify their findings. Thus the numbers of *notified* cases of food poisoning were about 100,000 for 1989, with a real incidence around ten times that figure, that is one million. The suffering, cost, burden on many services, and loss of working hours are all substantial.

10 *The Licensed Trade*

The centralised fermentation of beers, lagers and cider is one of the successes of the food industry. Beer and related drinks are technically food, although their nutritional content leaves a fair amount to be desired, being almost entirely carbohydrate! The reasons for the success of this operation are, first, the processes have been well researched; secondly, the procedures in the fermentation used are inherently safe; thirdly, careful monitoring and testing is performed; and fourthly, those responsible for sale to the public are well trained. High quality products, such as the superior versions of real ale, are also amenable to the system, and it is exceedingly rare for anything to go wrong.

The reason for the intrinsic safety of fermented drink is that after the addition of yeast, the sugars or starches present are changed into alcohol and acid. Acidity is measured on a logarithmic scale, known as pH. A neutral pH, meaning that the fluid is neither acid nor alkaline, is given a figure of 7.0. When acidity rises the pH drops logarithmically, so that each drop by a whole unit represents a tenfold increase in acidity. Therefore a pH of 5.0 is ten times more acid than a pH of 6.0. Most bacteria stop growing at a pH of 4.5 or below. Most beers, lagers and ciders have a final pH between 3.7 and 4.2, so are distinctly hostile to food poisoning bacteria. The alcohol and other substances, such as hop oils, may also contribute to the antibacterial properties of these drinks. Put another way, beer is an antiseptic. If mistakes do occur it is likely to be with the early stages of fermentation. For example, if the yeast was contaminated with a bacterium that could outgrow it, then the usual products—acid and alcohol—would not be formed. So by very simple chemical tests, these unwanted bacteria can be detected.

Home-made beer sometimes gets into difficulties if it is made under dirty conditions so that bacteria can compete for nutrients with the addition of the yeast at the beginning.

The brewing yeast is carefully adapted to grow under acidic conditions and at room temperatures. So at the end of fermentation, any residual yeast settles to the bottom of the vat or barrel and the drink becomes clear. However, there will probably be some yeasts invisibly present in the clear drink, and they can sometimes be tasted. There is no danger on drinking this as they do not survive in the human body and do not cause disease.

Sometimes during transport, barrels of beer, etc., can be shaken so that the bottom sediment of yeasts is dispersed through the drink which can appear cloudy on serving. This is not aesthetically appealing, but is safe. One wonders whether some of the very dark beers are designed to overcome the complaint of cloudy beer!

Occasionally other growths can occur in dirty piping; these may occasionally be due to the few bacteria particularly well adapted to growth at high acidity, and may cause some unpleasant tastes or even sickness. This explains the good bar practice of regularly cleaning the pipes, and flushing through and discarding (hopefully!) the first pint or so at the start of serving.

The recent interest in low alcohol beers and lagers raises questions over their safety. If the product has been prepared in the usual way, and then the alcohol removed by, say, boiling, then the acidity of the product should be high, and it should be safe. If the product has not been fermented sufficiently to generate adequate acid to prevent the growth of bacteria, then problems could result from subsequent contamination.

Other drinks with high alcohol content such as wines are also highly acidic. The typical alcohol content of beers, lagers and ciders varies from 2.5 per cent to five per cent, and that of wine nine to eleven per cent by volume. These concentrations of alcohol in themselves will not prevent all bacteria from growing, but with high acidity the bottled or canned products should be safe for months or years.

With spirits, the alcohol content of around 40 per cent is itself capable of stopping the growth of all bacteria and yeasts and can therefore keep almost indefinitely.

There are always snags with any system. With the brewing industry, success and profitability have given enormous power to a relatively few conglomerates. Although in some areas this is gradually being eroded, such power has resulted in problems of monopoly of suppliers to tied houses—the public houses owned and controlled by the brewers. The customer can be faced with lack of choice, not just in the alcoholic beverages but in other products whose sale is also under the brewers' control, directly or indirectly. Elsewhere, it has been suggested that greater choice for the customer can create problems of supply and storage of more items. So perhaps a fairly narrow range of fermented drinks in any one public house is the ideal, as far as safety and quality are concerned. We can't have it all ways!

The success of centralised production of fermented products has been stressed because it would appear to be the one important example of how an apparently perishable food can be provided safely by this means. Of course, beer is not really a perishable item, but rather a preserved one. However, brewing and hotel groups have begun to use this approach for other products, with all the marketing paraphernalia, and for genuinely perishable food the results can be disastrous; that fermented drinks are substantially different from food is beginning to dawn on the trade.

Many of the problem types of food involve the cook-chill genre, which are not suitably preserved or robust enough to withstand the treatment they receive. The first and probably most important snag is that, unlike fermented drinks, food cannot be tested reliably for safety at the point of production. Any potentially contaminating bacteria may be present in too small numbers to be detected then. However, following lengthy distribution and storage, these bacteria could increase to dangerous numbers. Secondly, if food is tested at the place of production, the complete results will not be available until after it has been dispatched or even consumed. The problems of rapid distribution and temperature control in lorries have already been stressed. The facilities and care over storage and reheating at the point of sale also cause concern. Much of the profit from this type of food will go to the brewery, and it may be expecting too much for the publican, particularly a salaried manager, either to know the risks involved with the food, or always to be motivated to ensure that correct procedures are followed.

Even if these problem areas were overcome, it would still be almost impossible for the brewery to comply with the Department of Health's guidelines of just three clear days of cold-holding, and at a temperature of between $0^{\circ}C$ and $3^{\circ}C$.

The second general concern is that the concept of centralised production and local reheating will determine the type of food available. The current fashion for jacket potatoes with various fillings, such as chili con carne, is determined by experience that such food is relatively 'resistant' to the system—that is, it survives with little loss of quality, at least in the short term. Similarly, the virtual disappearance of freshly cooked vegetables from many menus indicates that these foods fare badly with centralised production and long cold-holding followed by reheating. This is particularly noticeable with brassicas. There is loss of texture and loss of colour, the product becoming slimy or limp and often ochre-coloured. The smell is not appealing because of the generation of substances from decomposing unsaturated fatty acids. Hence the need for the salad garnish, seemingly ever popular—at least from the view of the food providers. The small heap of ageing, boring limp lettuce, with slices of under-ripe tomatoes and raw onions, is much more convenient to produce than cooked vegetables! What is more, because they are not often eaten, they can be used again and again (let us hope not, but I am a suspicious person)!

Many people have not been aware of these changes. One effect of this system is that there may be no facilities for primary cooking on site, which must reduce the ability to prepare specific items on request. Try ordering a particular dish without a sauce! If this is not possible, the whole item has probably been bought in frozen or chilled and reheated. If it is possible, then the component items may have been prepared and assembled there.

Let us now consider some particular types of food.

Pizzas

Pizzas (or more correctly pizze) are a good example of increasing availability because of the use of centralised production. Items of food now labelled as 'pizza' have become increasingly variable, and a few years ago it would not have been possible even to consider some items optimistically identified as 'pizza' as being anything of the sort.

Pizzas are generally made or assembled in a variety of ways. The traditional method, now practised only by *bona fide* Italian restaurants, involves the preparation of the whole item, base and topping, to order. The base dough rises little and the appeal is the freshness in the real sense, and the honesty of the item. Another method involves the previous production of the pizza at a central kitchen, with sale at the retail outlets. The pizza can be eaten cold or can be reheated. There is evident loss of quality, and the particular problem is that the base can go hard. The use of dough that produces a more aerated or bread-like texture and survives this treatment better than the traditional base has circumvented this problem. This explains why the third variant uses the bread-like base from a central production unit for local supplementation of toppings according to the customer's choice. The distribution and storage of these bases is made either in a chilled or in a frozen state. Some such pizza bases can be prepared at each retail site near to the time of eating, to be finished according to the customer's preference. The fourth example of the growing pizza genre is the supermarket species, with cooked bread-like base and largely uncooked top, although some ham, etc., will have been cooked.

It is difficult in the home to achieve a likeness to the real item, mainly because domestic ovens do not get hot enough. One recent development is the 'French bread pizza' which, as the name implies, consists of red and yellow material smeared onto the top of a bread-like substance in the shape of several inches of French bread. There is absolutely nothing of the freshness and smell of French bread. A major provider of these is British Rail. After a brief massacre in the microwave, the base tends towards hardness and the top to stickiness.

The development of this type of pizza seems to represent everything that is wrong about our approach to food. The prime determinant of the type offered is the availability of new food technology, centralised production and a comprehensive supply to many outlets all over the country. For some time, the memory of the real thing may linger and ensure adequate sales. This memory can be reinforced by massive pictures at the restaurant, reminding us how we used to see the food, and also by pictures on the packet—usually opaque, to prevent inspection of the actual product. For this particular food, the chief complaints are of poor quality for the high cost, rather than one of safety.

Pies, Pasties, Sausages

Meat pies, Cornish pasties, pork pies and sausages are still fairly popular as a pub meal. However, there is a suspicion that the popularity of these may be waning. It goes without saying that for items containing beef, readers should refresh themselves of material in Chapter 6. Two points about beef should be stressed. One is that the word 'beef' is not synonymous with joints of beef or steak. It includes other edible components, hopefully not those offal organs that should have been removed; there are diverse parts of the animal that still get into 'beef'. Moreover, pies and sausages will often contain the products from the elderly cow, slaughtered at the end of lactation. The second point is that some products, such as pies and sausages, although ostensibly labelled as 'pork' because pig products are the major meat constituent, can also contain some beef material. There is a need to make labels explicit in this area. However, to ensure that every product contains items only of the specified origin would be difficult to enforce. This explains why worries over beef appear to have had a general effect on consumption of many items containing processed meat, even though not ostensibly beef.

However, the real point of mentioning these products is to highlight that, if prepared or stored badly, there is a risk from food poisoning—of the acute bacterial variety. Products which have been cooked or reheated should not be kept warm for long—two hours should be the outside. After that they should be in a properly cold refrigerator. Placing these products on a cold shelf typically covered with tiles, with open access to the environment, is not a satisfactory means of refrigeration.

The problem has been aggravated by the abolition of the pub closing period in the afternoon. This did encourage unused heated food to be discarded. Consider now the plight of the publican who cooks or warms these products in preparation for trade beginning at mid-day. He puts his wares in a hot cabinet that is frequently opened, so the temperature is not high enough to restrain food poisoning bacteria from growing. The Department of Health believes that such stored food items should at least be at 63°C. This is a surprisingly high temperature which may make the food feel too hot to eat. The lunch-time pub customers arrive in dribs and drabs during the late morning and afternoon. If hot food is seen or smelt it may be purchased. So when does the publican discard his very profitable stock? From where does he receive advice? Where are the regulations? With luck a friendly visit from a local Environmental Health Officer will help, but in general there is little education or legal basis for this education to ensure safe handling of such food.

In conclusion, the continued increase in the popularity of 'eating-out' has been seized upon by the licensing trade as a means of optimising its facilities for this purpose. Some of the food items are of poor quality at the point of consumption. The choice is often determined by the technology used, rather than by what the customer wants. The whole system is not subject to adequate controls, and the consumer should identify the 'history' of the product before making his selection. The range of food items available in public houses could well be expanded. Sandwiches and rolls can and should be made to order.

11 *Microwave 'Ovens'*

The appeal of microwave ovens is easy to understand. These are first seen as an electric or electronic device required for modern living; they can have elaborate programmable controls. There may even be displayed yet another digital clock that is so important when all the others have broken down simultaneously! They are sold along with televisions, washing machines and 'old-fashioned' cookers. The modern household is incomplete without a microwave; their absence from the home denotes some sort of failure in the family. The advertisements from television and colour supplements are seductive. The cooked food *looks* most appetising. The recipe books given away with each model tell you that all your cooking is simply managed in a little box, and so quickly. They also pander to the British inferiority complex, since many are manufactured abroad. So, it is no wonder that clever marketing has sold microwave ovens so successfully to the British public, with more than half of all households now proud owners. Apparently more microwaves per head of population have been sold in the United Kingdom than in any other country.

The makers of convenience meals also have a direct vested interest in the devices. That the instructions on the glamorous cardboard boxes in which these meals are sold may be either confusing or irrelevant to your model seems to matter little.

The first moments of disillusionment come when you find that it is not possible to create a meal for a family in just one box—they seem only able to cook one item at a time! One may need as many as four to do the job! The next doubts are raised by finding that the properties of some foods are changed by the microwave. Some items become unexpectedly hard, or else they can go soggy. Then prepared meals seem incapable of being heated uniformly. But still, nothing is perfect, surely the benefit of letting the kids reheat their own burger or pizza justifies anything. They don't complain. (Children don't seem to complain of anything; they have been quick to accept the new technology.) It's only fussy parents and hypercritical neurotic food writers who impart doubts over what is a revolution, if not *the* revolution, in convenience eating.

One wonders how many people are privately disillusioned with microwaves, but don't want to admit they were hoodwinked into their purchase. If necessary a stoical front can be presented; after all, MAFF says at least some are all right, the food industry says they are necessary, and their presence can be observed in almost any restaurant, public house, canteen, railway station or, more recently, garage. Perhaps we should learn to enjoy microwaved chips and soggy, limp pastry.

However, serious safety fears will not go away; indeed, they are tending to increase. In this short chapter, we shall look at how microwaves work, then at these safety fears, and finally ask for what items the ovens should be used. Devotees of microwaves may be in for a shock.

Action of Microwaves

The waves produced in a microwave oven are generated by a magnetron. This type of generator is similar to those emitting radar for military purposes—indeed, microwaves and radar are similar, being extremely short electromagnetic radiation. The radiation emerges from the magnetron and is aimed towards the expected positioning of food items. However, many of the waves will miss the food. When this happens they are bounced off the inside surfaces of the walls of the 'oven' and off the inside of the door. The box is manufactured to withstand this without heating up. Gamma rays for heating food are somewhat different: they do not bounce, but are similar to microwaves in that heat is also generated as a result of their collision with atoms in the food. The microwaves then, either directly or indirectly, interact with the food. They will pass through most plastics, cardboards and glass. If these materials become hot, it is usually a result of heat being conducted from the food to the container or plate.

Exactly how microwaves generate heat and what happens in atomic terms when the wave collides with the food are not yet certain. Some molecules, such as those in water, appear to be particularly good at dissipating the wave. The end result is that the energy of the wave, having reacted with the food, is lost and heat is formed at the point of physical interaction.

Microwave ovens are said to be efficient in that to heat, say, 100ml (about four fluid ounces) of water, requires much less electric current than to heat 100ml of water in a conventional oven. This is because much of the heat in a conventional oven is wasted in heating air and the oven casing. About 50 per cent of the energy going into activating the magnetron in a microwave ends up as heat in the food.

One immediate and important consequence of this is that the greater the size of the food item, the more energy is required for heating. In practice this means longer exposure and is a serious limitation on the usefulness of microwave ovens, particularly when it is realised that prolonged treatment of the surface of food items can result in damaging effects before adequate heating of the inside has been achieved. In effect, it is usually just the outside inch (or even less) of the food that is heated directly by the microwave, with penetration of heat into the centre of large items occurring by conduction (as occurs in heating the contents of a saucepan on a cooker). The notion that microwaves heat more thoroughly than conventional cookers, or heat from the inside outwards, is quite erroneous.

The power generated by magnetrons varies according to design. Commercial microwaves may deliver more wave energy than domestic models, but their principle of action is the same. In use, and particularly with regard to time, the initial heating of the surface of food can indeed be rapid, but the need for thorough heating of the centre of relatively large items may require a long standing time—that is the time needed after turning off the power so that surface heat can penetrate into the centre. The hot surface will also lose heat outwards into the air, or into the container or plate. So, with a substantial standing time, the outside may start cooling significantly, and it is by no means certain that the inside of the food item will ever become sufficiently hot. Moreover, the nature of the food critically determines the degree of surface and central heating. The need for standing time may be such that the required length of total time of cooking is not substantially different from a conventional oven.

The use of a rotating plinth does improve slightly the evenness of surface heating, but the basic problem of heat penetration with large items remains.

Safety Worries
There are two types of safety concern over microwaves. One is the problem of certain destruction of possibly dangerous bacteria and the other is the generation of chemicals that might be harmful. Both these problems arise from the nature of the microwave oven itself and the way it is used. It is not really a question of whether some models are safe and others dangerous. Of course, so far as the danger with bacteria is concerned, the problem will be aggravated by the use of a low-energy model when a high-output is needed. However, a low-energy model used for, say six minutes, may be no more or less dangerous than a

high-output model used for three minutes. At the end of 1989, MAFF produced a list of recommended domestic models based on energy output. The implication was that models not on that list were unsatisfactory, but of course the crucial question that matters is *how* the device is to be used. To produce such a list calls into question the sanity not just of Ministers, but of their civil servants and their 'scientific' advisers.

Bacterial Problems

There are three main factors that determine whether certain bacteria in food are killed by heating. One is the nature of the food; another is the height of temperature reached; and the last is the length of time of heating. For example, pasteurisation of milk, which is aimed at removing possibly dangerous bacteria, is achieved by heating it to 63°C for 30 minutes, or 71.7°C for 15 seconds. The microwave has an inevitable problem compared with slower cooking methods; almost by definition its use is associated with only a short episode of heating. The next problem is uneven heating. Many prepared dishes for microwave heating are either square or rectangular; when rotated on a platform these are bound to produce inequalities in heating, even near the outside. Then, finally, the heat may simply not be able to penetrate into the middle of the item for long enough without making the outside of the product inedible. Dr Stephen Dealler in the Department of Microbiology at the University of Leeds has tried in vain to cook a haggis satisfactorily with a microwave, despite exhortations on the packet that it can be achieved. Always the outside becomes hard and charred before the inside gets hot enough to kill possible bacteria. We have studied a variety of prepared cook-chill meals inoculated with listeria and salmonella. Despite using 'Gummer-approved' models and following the instructions pedantically, in about 80 per cent of tests at least some of the bacteria survived.

We have told the manufacturers of microwaves our findings. Their response was to advise us, and the public, to stir the food while it was being cooked, presumably to distribute the surface heat into the centre. This, even with an item of soup-like consistency, is not that easy, but with many items it is not possible at all. First, the covering film would have to be removed; this could well cause spitting of the food around the oven with the trouble of subsequent cleaning. Was not reducing washing up one of the reasons for the microwave oven in the first place?

But there are more problems. Many items simply cannot be stirred. How, for example, do you stir a cook-chilled bread and butter pudding while it is being cooked?

For microbiological safety, we have concluded that microwave ovens should not be used for cooking any item if it requires the cooking to confer safety. This therefore excludes primary cooking of many meat and poultry products and reheating of cook-chill products.

Chemical Dangers

The second safety worry concerns the possible effect of newly formed chemicals on long-term human health. It must be pointed out that such danger has not been proven because there has been insufficient time for most of the theoretical problems to appear. And it is a quite legitimate view to take that, unless such dangers have been proven, we should assume microwaves are safe. As with so many other issues, notably BST, BSE and food irradiation, the central issue is one of philosophy. Should we require food producers and processors (and microwave ovens are found within this camp) to provide evidence of safety, or should those who represent consumer well-being have to establish the existence of danger?

The question of safety of microwaves is very similar to that of gamma rays in that, with both, the nature of the new chemicals is not adequately defined, nor is the effect of these on human health, particularly in the long term.

Put another way, we could consider that because microwaves have been accepted without this proof of safety, we should also accept the use of gamma rays. Alternatively, the doubts over microwaves could fuel those over gamma rays.

So what are the long-term worries with microwaves? There are three pieces of evidence. The first is that male workers exposed to electromagnetic radiation in the United States have a higher than expected incidence of cancer of the male breast. This work is still somewhat preliminary, and in order to define a cause-and-effect relationship, it will be desirable to see if the degree of increase in cancer incidence relates to the dose of the exposure—as, for example, the number of cigarettes smoked correlates directly with the risk of lung cancer. It is also necessary to look at more control groups, and other diseases in those exposed.

Microwaves are, of course, a type of electromagnetic radiation, and as a result of largely emotional fears over the years, most models have well-fitting doors that reflect the waves inwards with little escaping. We might be reassured that, to all intents and purposes, the operator will not be exposed to radiation. However, we cannot be reassured by this because the changes in the body of people exposed directly to electromagnetic radiation must be chemical in nature. There is no reason to doubt that such changes could occur in microwave-heated food, and that those chemicals would enter the body subsequently. After all, 'we are what we eat'! At least, that is so up to a point.

The next observation of note resulted from work performed in Austria, and published in December 1989. The doctors showed that microwave treatment of milk altered the three-dimensional structure of amino acids from the natural form to a mirror image of them not found to any extent in the human body. Amino acids are the small building blocks of proteins and enzymes that control all our body functions. It is not known how many of those 'unnatural' amino acids are generated in food as a rule, nor is it known whether the body can always change these back into the usual shape. Certainly, some tissues can do this, but can those of the unborn baby? If the mother ate these products they could well be distributed widely in her tissue, including that of the baby. Further work is needed, and at present we must state that the significance of this effect is not known.

Thirdly, my colleague, Dr Stephen Dealler, has shown that microwaves have a particular propensity to react with ions, such as common salt or monosodium glutamate (MSG). This study was initiated to try to find an explanation for the particularly poor central heating of convenience meals. What appears to happen is that the salt (and also sugar) and MSG react very strongly with the microwaves on the extreme surface of the food which gets very hot—even hotter than usual—and the penetration inwards is much less than through controlled foods such as mashed potato. So heavily salted food heated with microwaves has an exaggerated difference in the temperature between the hot outside and the cold centre.

The nature of the chemicals released as a result of the dissipation of the microwaves after collision with these ions is not known, so their potential toxicity is not capable of definition.

Use of Microwaves
The appeal of food is very much an individual judgement. There are no blacks or whites, rather shades of grey. If anyone wants to like something, he or she will. So, in this section the views expressed are very subjective. However, these are not just my personal opinions, but rely on those of a number of colleagues, and indeed on the testing of many microwave models. There is a number of microwave ovens combined with other devices. These are excluded from this discussion; they may, however, go some way

towards answering the criticism. The combination model without the microwave facility might in itself be of use!

But first let us try and identify quality food cooked by the microwave. First on the list must be some vegetables, such as peas, beans, brassicas, carrots, onions and peppers. With care and presentation, these can be excellent. Timing is important: cooking for too long can make carrots hard. The problems develop when vegetables are cooked with other items in the same oven, but if the cooking time is short the texture can be firm and the colours well retained, as well as the vitamins.

Making gravies, and sauces such as bread sauce directly in the china boat is satisfactory for quality. Similarly, the production of hot drinks poses few problems.

Reheating of plated meals for latecomers is a quick alternative to the conventional oven, but items can lose texture, particularly pastry.

Microwave ovens are frequently recommended for defrosting frozen food in preparation for conventional cooking. The low settings are used, but it must be appreciated that this in reality is light cooking from the outside inwards. Large items may not be adequately defrosted in the middle although the surface is nearly cooked. Small frozen items can, anyway, be cooked directly, without defrosting. This use of microwave ovens requires care, particularly for frozen poultry. My advice on frozen poultry is to defrost in a container slowly in a refrigerator over one or two days, taking care not to spill the juices—a rich source of potentially dangerous bacteria (see Chapter 12).

Now for some of the 'problem' foods. Jacket potatoes have often been the status symbol of the microwave. True, they can be cooked in half to a third of the time they take in a conventional oven. True, the heat penetrates well into the centre of medium-size potatoes. But is the quality the same as the conventional oven-baked potato? The main difference is in the skin, with the microwaved potato having a thin, soft tasteless skin, and the oven-baked potato skin being possibly burnt, crusty or at least crisp, with some interesting flavours just under the skin. The microwave enthusiast will argue that many people don't eat the skin of baked potatoes. This may be true. But the oven-baked jacket potato has a wonderful smell, giving pleasure to the whole meal. The microwaved potato has much less smell and taste.

One of the problems with most microwave ovens is that there is no facility to keep items hot. In which case, the conventional oven may need to be kept hot anyway—surely a better choice for jacket potatoes!

New potatoes do not fare well in the microwave. They are edible, but it is difficult to obtain the uniform creamy effect obtained from standard boiling. Their surface tends to dry and go hard.

For breakfast, microwave-cooked sausages and bacon seem to present one of two choices—either limp or hard. With intermittent stirring, scrambled eggs can resemble almost the saucepan variety, but certainly are not any better—at least in our view.

Increasingly, foods are being prepared specially for the microwave. Expert cooks may get them to succeed, but my own attempt with 'microwave chips' which ended up either hard or soggy, and always with a stale taste, is apparently fairly typical.

It seems that few foods are really improved by microwave cooking; many are ruined.

*　　　*　　　*

So where does this leave us with microwave ovens? Are they safe? What should they be used for? Are the uses mentioned recommended? The answer to these questions is—we don't know.

If side-effects from eating microwaved food do develop in the long term, the people most at risk must be children and pregnant women. The risk is also likely to be related to the extent of microwave use. Perhaps, as an occasional adjunct to the family meal, the risks may be minimal.

In summary, microwave ovens have only recently been scrutinised for safety. That the generation of heat is a by-product from the interaction of these short 'radar' waves with molecules in the food explains why most heat is generated on the surface of the food. The long-term safety of these ovens has not been established.

Unquestionably, the quality of some food items such as pastry fare badly in the simple microwave oven. Others, such as vegetables, can excel. Perhaps we should view microwaves as a minor adjunct to the standard methods of cooking, rather than attempting to utilise a microwave for all our cooking. The practicality of the comprehensive microwaved family meal seems to be an overoptimistic claim by many of the glossy recipe books.

As far as microbiological safety is concerned, the message is now becoming clear: slow cooking is safer than fast. The old-fashioned solid-fuelled or the newer electric or gas cookers will continue to provide the predominant facility for cooking.

12 *Food Safety in the Home*

If one believed all the propaganda from the food producers and the Ministry of Agriculture, most of our food problems would be attributed to the incompetent consumer! It is of course true that the consumer may represent the last defence against food contamination, and if the food is not adequately cooked, food poisoning might result. The distribution of leaflets in 1989 by the government, giving instructions on food safety, was an implicit criticism of the consumer. The supermarkets' hot line was an attempt to reassure, so that if problems did develop, the cause would be seen not to be the responsibility of the food producer.

One interesting question which has not been answered is that if the consumer purchases contaminated food, fails to cook it thoroughly and then develops food poisoning, who is responsible for this in law? Consider a particular example, of food poisoning resulting from eating chicken contaminated with salmonella or campylobacter, which was not cooked very thoroughly. First the farmer might be held responsible; or the slaughterer who could have caused the contamination. The distributor or the retailer could also be considered guilty. Perhaps it is the consumer's fault, or possibly the makers of the cooking equipment which did not achieve adequate destruction of the bacteria.

Very few cases of this type have been tested in the courts, so the issues are still somewhat unclear. However, it seems a reasonable starting premise that the consumer has every right to eat food in any way he or she prefers. For example, raw liver can be recommended for specific dietary purposes. It would seem that as long as the consumer takes proper care over the storage and handling of food, it is not (or certainly *should* not be) his responsibility to cook it in such a way as to guarantee safety. Rather the responsibility lies with the retailer—that is, usually the supermarket. So if food poisoning did result from eating, say, a chicken cooked in a microwave, and that chicken had been stored correctly and not been contaminated in the home, the legal responsibility should be with the retailer. The problem in practice is that it is very difficult to prove in any one instance that a mishap has not occurred in the home. Incidentally, if the retailer were found responsible, he could well make a claim against the suppliers.

In this chapter, I shall describe the ideal ways of handling food in the home. Regrettably, such meticulous care is needed on account of the high probability of contamination of raw food. If this advice is followed, then the consumer should feel that he or she has done his or her best to avoid poisoning the family or friends. It will also provide a useful base from which to initiate legal action against the food suppliers. Many people believe that many of the problems of food contamination will not be solved without resorting to legal action in order to establish some principles.

The Refrigerator
Most modern homes, including the kitchen, are centrally heated. In older times the kitchen was situated to the north of the house and there might well have been cool sculleries, larders or cellars. The problem today is that for the storage of perishable food one of two options exists: the food is either kept at room temperature or it is held in the refrigerator. This generates problems for food which should ideally be kept cool rather than cold, and for this reason many people use the refrigerator to accommodate a

large variety of items at temperatures which cannot be satisfactory for all of them.

It would seem better to use the refrigerator exclusively for the really perishable items, where a very low temperature is needed. Other items—for example, vegetables, hard cheeses and eggs—which can be stored at room temperature so long as it is on the cool side, are preferably kept out of the refrigerator.

So what food items should go into the refrigerator, and for how long?

First, consider raw food, for example any uncooked meat, poultry or fish. These must be assumed to contain bacteria, including some possibly dangerous ones, and should be kept in the refrigerator pending cooking and eating. Each item should be individually wrapped and placed on the bottom shelves, either on plates or in containers to prevent any possibility of fluid or juices escaping and contaminating other food.

Next, consider any food that has already been cooked, and left-overs which need to be kept. These should be wrapped and placed in the refrigerator. Such items include cooked meats, pies, vegetables, opened cans, mayonnaise and other condiments.

Milk, dairy products and soft cheeses should also be stored in the refrigerator. Butter and margarines which are low in water—that is, those which are not 'low fat'—can be stored for some time at room temperature, but there is a risk of decomposition of the fats increasing, so the refrigerator provides a useful aid. All these particular items are satisfactory at storage temperatures of between 0ºC and 3ºC, and in order to maintain this temperature a thermometer should be placed in the middle of the refrigerator and the temperature checked the first time the door is opened in the morning. After the door has been opened the temperature is bound to rise briefly, say for thirty minutes or so, and then fall back to the cold level. This will not adversely affect the safety and quality of the food. The point of taking the morning temperature is that it will give the baseline temperature which will persist for most of the day. It is certainly possible that some refrigerators are unable to achieve this, and indeed some of the dials or gauges that are present will do nothing to identify the exact temperature.

Almost all refrigerators used today contain a coolant consisting of chlorofluorocarbons (CFCs). There is good reason to believe that the release of these into the atmosphere throughout the world has been responsible for damaging atmospheric ozone, particularly at the Poles, and many people are worried that their own domestic refrigerator or indeed deep-freezer could be responsible for this. In practice escape of these gases is exceedingly unlikely in the home; the real risk occurs during the manufacture of the refrigerator and most especially in the disposal. If changing the refrigerator, it is important to identify the best possible way of disposal of the old one, and a telephone call to the local Environmental Health Department could be helpful.

When food items are placed in the refrigerator they should all be individually wrapped to prevent cross-contamination. There should also be enough space so that the wrapped items are not jammed together and all of them should be capable of being viewed. This is to prevent a potentially dangerous hidden item being kept for too long. The question of how long items should be kept in a refrigerator depends partly on the item and partly how cold it is, but as we have already seen there are at least five different types of bacteria that can grow at temperatures round about 3⁰C and can cause disease. It is essential to appreciate once again that the refrigerator is not the complete answer to all problems of food safety; rather it represents a temporary holding area for certain food items which would otherwise become dangerous if stored at higher temperatures. Prolonged storage in the refrigerator can be just as dangerous as a much shorter storage time at room temperature. I recommend the following storage times:

Raw meats. If these are subject to subsequent thorough cooking they can be stored between one and three days, and occasionally for longer. Some items, for example bacon and sausages, may well contain preservatives and these can be stored for longer still. Information to this effect should be on the packet.

Fish. This is best stored for less than 24 hours and ideally should be eaten on the day of purchase, since some of the bacteria that cause the formation of ammonia and other smells do grow at low temperatures. In general the optimum time for eating fish is between two and three days old. Before arrival at the retailers, fish will usually have been stored at temperatures of around 10°C for one or two days; this allows the maximum formation of flavour, but after about three days the unpleasant aromas can accumulate.

Left-overs. Cooked meats and vegetables, and open cans and other condiments, should in general not be kept for more than two days.

Some prepared items which should never be kept after the meal include gravies, sauces and custards that are made up from powders, because any bacteria present in the powder might recover during storage in the refrigerator. These products are quite safe to eat immediately after being constituted, but any remains should then be discarded.

It is a good general rule to clean out the refrigerator completely every week, removing all stains. There is usually no need to use antiseptics or bleaches. A good detergent should suffice, and after cleaning is is important to dry all the internal surfaces. Also check the door seals weekly, and make certain that the door can close satisfactorily.

If the fridge has an automatic defrost cycle, then it is particularly important to appreciate that food items should not be kept for too long. Those models without a defrost cycle should be defrosted once a week, and this provides a good opportunity to clear out all unused food items.

The Deep Freeze

In theory, the deep freeze is certainly a more desirable piece of equipment than the domestic refrigerator. The reason for this is that the ideal temperature of a deep freeze—that is, between -18°C to -23°C—stops the growth of all bacteria and all fungi and, moreover, there is a generous margin of safety. There are virtually no bacteria that grow below -5°C, and even the most cold-loving fungus stops growing at -10°C.

The preferred type of deep freeze is the floor-standing cabinet type with access from the top lid. Some of the upright deep freezers are combined with refrigerator units; these are not entirely satisfactory because it is difficult to keep the two adjacent compartments at ideal temperatures. Also, when the door of an upright freezer is opened the cold air literally tumbles out of it and this produces two effects. One is the requirement of more energy to maintain the cold temperature, and the other is a risk of the temperature rising to too high a level.

As with the refrigerator, it is a good idea to have a thermometer installed, and this could be checked weekly, the first time the lid is opened on that day.

When food is placed in the deep freeze all growth of bacteria and fungi ceases but they are generally not killed. There is one exception to this in that some campylobacter bacteria are permanently damaged by freezing. However, this does not occur reliably and you must make a general rule that you do not and should not consider that freezing bacteria kills them. Thus the safety of food associated with the use of the deep freeze depends on the amount of contamination of the food that occurs before it is put in the freezer, and also the possibility of contamination occurring after removal.

For this reason, the most potentially dangerous items associated with the deep freeze are those which are eaten without further cooking. For example, if you placed unwrapped raw poultry adjacent to ice cream in the freezer, it would be quite possible for bacteria from the poultry to contaminate the ice cream which would then be eaten without being cooked and could generate food poisoning. So as a good general rule, as with the refrigerator, raw food items must be kept wrapped and separated from cooked food items and from items which will be eaten without further cooking.

As to how long food items can be kept, it will depend on what they are and on the nature of the freezer. So long as the temperature is in the range of -18°C to -23°C, the length of storage affects the quality of the food rather than its safety; the star guide on the packets is helpful, although it is entirely up to the consumer to decide how long he or she would like to keep an item. It is a good policy to have a rotation of stock and to label items made in the home with dates, having established the length of time a food item can be considered acceptable.

Some deep freezes will need to be defrosted occasionally and a simple policy would be to do this every three months. It would be a reasonable plan to try and use up any stored frozen food at this time and then restock. Problems can come with power cuts, and if this should happen the installation of a thermometer could be particularly useful. Of course, if the power supply to the deep freeze is cut off, it is essential that you do not open the lid, and hopefully the restoration of power within 24 hours will not cause permanent damage. If you are concerned about the safety of inadvertently thawed-out food the best procedure to adopt is as follows: As soon as the power supply is restored, open the lid and check the top items. These are more likely to be defrosted than those underneath, and if they are still frozen as judged by touch and the presence of ice crystals, then you can reasonably assume that there is no danger. If you have installed a thermometer and this reads below -5°C, then you have firm evidence that the loss of power has not caused dangerous thawing of items. However, it must be appreciated that once there has been a phase of higher temperatures which has lasted several hours, the subsequent length of storage may be limited. When in doubt, discard any suspect items.

Thawing Frozen Foods
Whilst in many ways a deep freeze is preferable to the refrigerator for storage, the problems come with the thawing of large items in preparation for cooking. If a large item is taken out of the deep freeze and the inside is still at a very low temperature when you want to start cooking, it inevitably follows that there will be a problem of heat penetration into the centre. There may be pressures sometimes to rush the cooking, and this may aggravate the problem in that the outside of the food item can be burnt without adequate penetration into the centre.

One of the effects that this has on the optimum use of the deep freeze is that the best and safest items are of small size, and if you are preparing home-made products for the deep freeze, ideally you should make them as small as possible.

Let us consider, however, the use of the deep freeze for large items, and look at the correct procedure for defrosting and then cooking safety. When an item is thawed out there is a likelihood that fluid will emanate from it which will contain bacteria, so it is important that the product is kept in a polythene bag and placed in a container to confine any juices that might emerge on thawing. If, for example, poultry has been deep-frozen with the giblets inside, it will be very difficult to remove them at this stage. Rather, the whole item should be put in the bottom of a refrigerator so that the thawing is slow and thorough. The length of time required for complete thawing will vary with the size of the item, but it could be between one and three days. If the item is kept in the refrigerator for longer than is needed for thawing, there will be little risk of bacteria multiplying. In contrast, if it is thawed at room temperature, and if this is performed overnight, with the thawing complete half-way through the night, then during several hours there will be an opportunity for bacteria to multiply and produce toxins which may not be eliminated entirely by cooking.

If thawing is undertaken in the microwave oven, then it is important to follow the instructions very carefully, particularly the standing time that will permit the heat generated on the outside of the product to penetrate into the centre. In reality, thawing in the microwave is effectively light cooking. If the food item is subsequently cooked in a conventional oven, then the outside may become too dry before the inside is well cooked. It seems that, overall, the use of the refrigerator with the product confined within a container is by far the most satisfactory method of thawing a large item. However, because of the length of time needed, the menus have to be planned some time in advance.

Kitchen Hygiene
There are certain principles involved in the safe handling and preparation of food. Probably the most important single rule is always to keep raw food, whether it be meat, fish, poultry or vegetables, completely separate from cooked food, so that there is no opportunity for bacteria that may be present on the raw food from actually coming into contact with cooked food which is usually eaten without reheating. If this single rule is remembered, then the risks from food poisoning will be reduced hopefully to very small levels. The problem arises when accidental

contact of cooked food with raw food occurs, or indeed when you realise that the same knife has been used for both items. The question of what should be done is not always straightforward. The best advice is to remove the part of the cooked food that has been soiled. Alternatively, the cooked food should be reheated before being eaten. This is not as important for some items as for others. Most fresh, washed vegetables which can, of course, be eaten raw, would not provide a major danger, whereas processed meat and poultry products certainly would.

It also follows that in order to achieve the general separation of raw and cooked food, the areas for their preparation should be apart, with, preferably, designated areas for each. Similarly, if you can manage it, you should try to keep knives or other utensils specifically for use with either raw or cooked food. This may not be possible in practice, and indeed it may make kitchen procedures too complex. The alternative, which most people adopt, is that after raw food has been manipulated in any way, whether cutting, chopping or handling, then the utensils should be thoroughly cleaned and dried before being used for cooked food.

The risk of spreading bacteria from cooked items to raw items is small. If cooked items are prepared and handled before raw items as a matter of principle, this in itself will reduce any risk of contamination.

There has been much publicity over the dangers of chopping boards. If food fragments do become wedged into crevices and these are kept at warm temperatures, then the bacteria will multiply to large numbers and might contaminate other foods. So the very important practice over hygiene of chopping boards is physically to make certain that all food debris is removed from crevices with, for example, a good scrubbing brush. After cleaning, the chopping board should be dried very carefully. If tiny amounts of bacteria and food products are still in the crevices, the final drying should go a long way towards destroying them. Physical removal of debris is much more important than the use of antiseptics and bleaches, which may not actually penetrate deep into the crevices.

Another means by which unwanted bacteria can contaminate food is from the misuse of hand towels, and with the best will in the world, hand towels or teacloths are sometimes used to clean hands contaminated by blood from raw meat. Ideally, hand towels, tea towels and dishcloths should be used exclusively for their proper functions, and should be changed daily. They should be washed thoroughly in hot water, and completely dried before further use.

It is good policy to keep pet food separate from human food, since there is a small risk of uneaten pet food providing a reservoir for bacterial multiplication; if this occurred, contact with human food could be dangerous. So it is a good idea to keep the pet food and the utensils used in a separate area of the kitchen, where the pets eat.

Utensils used for slicing, grating or processing should be cleaned vigorously after use and then allowed to dry.

There is no need to use antiseptic or bleach in the kitchen at all. The important procedure for cleaning is mechanical removal of material. This may be helped by detergent. A detergent is a substance that helps the lifting of dirt and does not itself have any antibacterial activity. So in order to remove the unwanted bacteria and unwanted food debris, the two most important principles are physical removal followed by drying of the area so that any bacteria are destroyed. Deep crevices can develop sometimes, particularly around the sink. These can be difficult to clean out. This explains why it is sensible to keep the fabric of the kitchen smooth, without deep cracks in which food can survive. The presence of food debris can attract insects or other pests that might then transfer bacteria to food items intended for eating.

Similarly, all rubbish bins should be firmly lidded, and pets should not have access to food remains from the rubbish area.

Where food has accidentally been spilt from packets in cupboards, etc., it should be removed completely; even if it is dry, water in the environment will be taken up and provide the opportunity for bacteria to grow, and this will attract vermin, pets, and insects.

It is a good rule to avoid leaving any uncovered food in the open because of the possibility of flies and other pests alighting and transferring bacteria between the various items.

An important question is how long it is safe to leave cooked food out of the refrigerator. It can be stated fairly categorically that, so long as recently cooked food is not kept for longer than one-and-a-half hours at room temperature, it should be safe. This is a very short limit and is based on the knowledge that bacteria, once they have contaminated an item either from the air or from touch, usually go into a phase of suspended animation for around one-and-a-half hours or a little longer, and when in this phase they do not actually grow. Of course, some food items can be kept for much longer at room temperature, for example, hard cheeses and vegetables, which can be kept at room temperature for several days. The dangerous items are the cooked foods which contain a fair amount of moisture, such as cooked meats, rice, potatoes, fish, poultry, and egg-based products.

Personal Hygiene

Understanding personal hygiene is really a matter of common sense and is based on the knowledge that the human body contains bacteria which are usually harmless when present in or on us, but if they get into food their properties change and they can become dangerous. Indeed, many infections that we suffer from are due to the presence of our own normally harmless bacteria in the wrong place. The total number of bacteria in the human body is about 1,000 million million, and most of these are in our intestines. The biggest danger as far as food contamination goes is that we transfer the bacteria from our intestines to food.

The first reaction to this possibility may be one of disbelief, but unfortunately in reality this happens all too easily. The problem results from the properties of most types of toilet paper, which let bacteria through. More than a million bacteria can be present on the fingers without being visible. So the really important aspect of personal hygiene is, very simply, handwashing, in order to make quite certain that the bacteria which may have entered into crevices in the hands or around the fingernails are removed, and therefore cannot be transferred to food items.

Fingers and nails should be maintained in such a way as to make the washing easy. This suggests that nails should be cut short—which conflicts with pressures from fashion! Ideally, rings should be removed in order to wash hands thoroughly, although it is not the upper parts of the fingers that are likely to become contaminated but rather the tips, particularly round the nails.

Hands should be washed thoroughly after going to the lavatory, on entering the kitchen, and after handling raw meat, fish or poultry or other possibly contaminated food. A nail brush should be used and the hands should be carefully dried on a towel. Hands should also be washed when general cleaning up of the kitchen is carried out, including removal of dirt and uneaten pet food, cleaning round the sink, and emptying wastebins.

Insufficient emphasis has been placed in the past on the importance of the correct disposal of food from wastebins. It should be realised that bacteria in food in the wastebin, kept either in the kitchen or outside if the weather is warm, will multiply rapidly. If any contaminated food remnants come into contact with the fingers, then risks could occur; it is therefore very important to wash the hands after emptying the dustbin.

There has been an active debate about the best type of detergent to use on the hands and there are some who prefer the liquid soaps. These are not recommended because many of the liquid soaps permit bacteria to grow whereas the standard bar soap, which is kept dry after use, will discourage bacterial growth. The container for the soap should allow water to drain away after use. Nail brushes are essential to remove bacteria from the fingers, and after use they should be rinsed with hot water and allowed to dry. They should be replaced at intervals, say monthly. If two kitchen sinks are available, it is a good plan to use one sink entirely for handwashing and another for food preparation and dispersal. Of course, if the skin is cut or damaged, these lacerations and also any boils or other infections on the body should be covered. Hair should obviously be kept out of food and this accounts for the professional chef's hat!

During food preparation, much emphasis has been placed on the importance of handwashing, but another possible contaminating source is human hair touched accidentally by the hand. Placing parts of the hand in the mouth or touching the nose can introduce bacteria to the fingers, which can then contaminate the food.

Large numbers of bacteria can be found on dirty clothes, which could be transferred to the food environment. One point about personal hygiene that applies particularly to caterers is that if they have been suffering from any illness that might be causing diarrhoea, then problems of personal hygiene are much harder to control, so it makes good general sense either to take meticulous care over handwashing or to avoid preparing food items when suffering from diarrhoea.

If these precautions as a whole are followed and food items are stored as recommended here, then any food poisoning is exceedingly unlikely to be the consumer's fault.

13 Additives—
Do We Need Them?

During the last few years, most, but certainly not all, additives have been listed on the packets of processed foods. Whilst this has certainly provided helpful information, many people are not aware of what either 'E' numbers or specific chemicals actually mean as possible hazards, or why they are present in the food at all. Many books have been written on the subject of chemical additives; it is not the purpose of this chapter to review them all. Rather, the general requirement for so many additives is a further illustration of the deficiencies of our supermarket culture, where perishable items are required to be stored for too long. Some chemicals are entirely cosmetic and quite unnecessary. The elimination of additives would, at a stroke, require the abandonment of many unsatisfactory supermarket food items (also see Chapter 15).

Artificial Colourants
A colour may be added to food for a number of reasons. Perhaps the most understandable is to provide the consumer with the appropriate image of the product. For example, if a new margarine is prepared from pure white ingredients, it might not appeal to the shopper expecting margarine to be coloured yellow. Sometimes, the colour can be used to restore loss of the natural pigment during processing, such as loss of green colouring during canning. In other instances, colour can imply a flavour such as in assortments of sweets. Another use can be to mask the presence of some of the components of the food.

Some colour additives are unquestionably natural—that is, the identical substance occurs in unprocessed food. The green pigment chlorophyll is a good example, being found in all green vegetable produce. Other substances are artificial, in that they are made by chemical reactions. Tartrazine, the yellow dye incorporated into so many convenience and frozen foods, smoked fish, mayonnaise and orange and lemon drinks, has one of the widest uses of all artificial colourants. Other substances do not fall comfortably into either the natural or artificial category. Caramel is one of these and will be discussed on p. 193. It is increasingly being appreciated that even though a substance is found naturally, it cannot necessarily be used in unlimited amounts. Vitamin A (carotene) is one example.

Of all the food additives, colourants have received greatest justifiable criticism because their benefits seem either trivial or non-existent, and their potential hazards considerable. For this reason, since 1988, only three additive colours are permitted in baby food. These are riboflavine (E101) riboflavin-5-phosphate (E101a) and carotene (E160a). These substances are all naturally occurring and indeed are vitamins—that is, we require small amounts of these anyway in our diet. However, even with these, excessive intake may be undesirable. The worrying aspect of the ban on other additives in so-called baby food is that, while appearing to satisfy the active campaigners against the use of artificial colourants, in practice it achieves very little. Young children can be fed with items not manufactured specifically for them. Can you imagine an ice cream maker using tartrazine or quinoline yellow, or the red erythrosine, as colourants, and then labelling his products with the advice 'not suitable for children'?

Canthaxanthin and Salmon Farming
How many people have wondered where all the extra supplies of vividly coloured Scottish salmon have come

from? The answer, of course, is fish-farming and it is the use of the orange-red dye canthaxanthin that enables the whole operation to succeed.

In the wild, the life of the salmon alternates between the open sea and usually specific freshwater rivers, notably in Scotland, Ireland, Scandinavia and Canada. The pink colour of the flesh results from its natural diet which includes tiny pink-coloured organisms. To many people salmon is a very desirable food, whether fresh or smoked. Not only do they find the flavour and texture appealing, but the colour as well. It is also rich in protein and fish oils which are high in polyunsaturated fatty acids and almost certainly of benefit nutritionally. The polyunsaturated fats of fish are in part determined by their presence in their food.

Until the last ten years or so, salmon was viewed by most people as a justifiably expensive luxury. So too were chickens, turkeys and ducks many years ago. We have seen in Chapter 4 how the transition from free range to intensive production lowered the price of these, but at the expense of safety and quality. The status of salmon has also altered, with a reduction in price again being offset by concerns over safety and quality. At present, however, insufficient research has been undertaken into farmed salmon to be sure that safety risks do exist, or whether the quality has declined.

In the British Isles salmon is farmed mainly in Western Scotland and Ireland, usually by making artificial containment areas in sea lochs. There are exceptions: a few farms are inland, with seawater pumped to artificial lakes, and some farms are found outside these areas.

Whilst the farmed salmon in Scotland is sold as 'Scottish salmon', and is of course from a Scottish locality, the parentage of the farmed fish may be different from the wild, sometimes having some 'Norwegian blood'. The young fish reared are specifically adapted to surviving, if not flourishing, under farmed conditions.

During growth, the captive salmon are fed artificially with meal containing the reddish-orange dye canthaxanthin. Without this substance the flesh of the final product would be dirty white.

If the practice of feeding the reddish dye were to cease, the description of the fish as 'Scottish salmon' would immediately run into trouble. Many of the current purchasers of farmed salmon are unaware of its source, particularly the numerous overseas clients so impressed by the vivid orange-pink smoked products on sale at the airports and the retail outlets in Knightsbridge and elsewhere. The pallor of the flesh without the dye would not be acceptable. This is not to claim that the use of the pink dye is an attempt at deliberate deception; it is required for commercial reasons. Some readers, however, may not be able to distinguish between these motives!

Apart from the pink dye, there have been other concerns over the composition of the feed. One salmon farmer has complained about the presence of chicken feathers in the feed. The inference of this finding is fairly obvious and raises the whole question of the source of the salmon feed in general. If the feed is derived from poultry or animal offal, then the nutritional value of the fish may well have declined. This should be researched.

It is not surprising that rearing salmon under artificial conditions is associated with many fungal and bacterial infections and with infestations such as sea lice. In theory the use of the numerous chemicals needed for the control of these should not cause danger to man; any toxicity should be averted because of the required interval between the use of the drug and the harvesting of the fish. This may be difficult to achieve in practice, however, because of the need to add the drugs to the water, and there could be accidental exposure of fish held in enclosures adjacent to the site where the drugs are being used. Certainly confidence over the enforcement of withholding intervals must be much less than for drugs fed to land animals of birds.

There is an organo-phosphorous chemical, known as dichlorvos, which poses particular problems; although unfortunately, there appears to be no alternative to its use for the control of sea lice. The parasites are destroyed by paralysis, which explains the extreme danger to the human handlers, and when the salmon are treated there is a degree of damage to nearby sea creatures—even a risk that some salmon might contain traces of the drug at harvesting. The rate at which dichlorvos disintegrates in water varies with temperature and acidity, the greater time being required in cold, acid water. Theoretically, adequate time should elapse between the use of the drug and the harvesting of the treated fish, but accidents can happen and batches of nearby salmon on the point of harvesting could be accidentally exposed. What is certain is that dichlorvos is environmentally damaging, and it is no surprise that many ecological pressure groups are angry over its continued use.

Caramel
Much of the artificial brown colouring of food and drink comes from the use of caramel (E150). You can easily produce this yourself by heating dry sugar in a saucepan. It splutters and darkens as you stir, and when you add water you are left with a clear, dark brown solution. The problem with the caramel produced in the food industry is that it is not a single pure substance, but a variable mixture of chemicals, many of which have not been identified fully. Although caramel has been given an E number, it can be argued that it should not continue to be used as a colourant, since it is not known exactly which chemicals it contains, and the safety of all its component substances has not been tested, let alone established.

In practice, caramel is used to darken many foods, including beer, cola, sauces, biscuits, sweets, soups, chocolate, liquorice and cakes. Indeed, caramel-type products are generated almost every time pastry is baked, bread toasted, fudge or toffee made, and these have not been shown to cause any hazards. So it could be argued that caramel is 'natural' and does not 'deserve' an E number at all. But the counter-argument is that just because a substance or mixture of substances has been used for many years, this does not prove safety. It can also be argued that the identity of every additive to food should be known, and that all such substances should be tested for safety. However, exactly how this is to be achieved is not clear. It might be possible to purify and test one of the chief brown colours from caramel, but this would be extremely costly.

There is no simple solution to this dilemma. If the use of caramel were to be discontinued, the food industry would have to face questions about the exact chemical composition of other substances thought to be 'natural'. Even water may come under suspicion. Tap water is a dilute solution of various dissolved salts and gases and other chemicals. Were requirements made for all these to be identified, this would be an impossible task.

The caramel dilemma reveals the difficulty of knowing exactly where to draw the line between an acceptable and an unacceptable use of a food colourant.

Putting aside caramel for the moment, can proposals be made for any future use of colourants? Hitherto, any restrictions have not had any major impact on the sales of specific products—that is, the food industry has been well protected, with regulations limited chiefly to compulsory labelling.

The essential point concerning colourants is that they are not needed: they provide virtually no nutritional value, except the very few natural substances. Much of their use is aimed at inducing sensations in the consumer. Could we not accept that margarine may be white, and if necessary for sales, put the colourant into the packaging? Can there really be any justification for any artificial colourant at all?

The debate over the association of specific dangers and certain colourants such as tartrazine continues. Often danger is difficult to prove or quantify, but it is certain that no benefit can accrue from their use, as measured by nutritional or medical parameters.

Natural colourants, such as chlorophyll, should be controlled so that the final amount ingested presents a safe concentration, and as such should not really be viewed as additives in the general sense.

The question of caramel remains extremely difficult. It would appear to be one of the genuine cases where more research is justified. So often the need for research has been used by governments as ingenious delaying tactics to protect a commercially sensitive area. With caramel, the jury is still out. With other artificial colourants, there is no case for their continued use.

Antioxidants

The nutrients in certain foods tend to decompose during storage. One of the processes is described as oxidation, whereby oxygen in the air participates in a chemical reaction with substances in the food, resulting in the formation of new chemicals. The unsaturated fatty acids are most vulnerable to this reaction and generate two types of problem. One is the loss of desirable or even essential nutrients, and the other is the formation of new products that can have an unpleasant taste or smell.

The extent to which these chemical changes occur is affected by storage time, the temperature at which the food item is held, and the amount of oxygen available. Inserting products into packets where all air, and therefore oxygen, is excluded will stop oxidation. However, the use of vacuum packs generates other problems—for example, the red colour of meat products can become dark brown, and the absence of oxygen can permit growth of the dangerous bacterium *Clostridium botulinum*. For this reason, the food industry is experimenting with the use of different types of gases in packets to overcome these problems.

Keeping products deep-frozen will certainly reduce markedly the rate of oxidation, but at the temperatures at which chilled food is stored in practice—say 5^0C–10^0C—the chemical changes occur rapidly. In order to redress this problem, the industry has adopted one of two approaches—either to treat the unsaturated fats chemically to reduce their rate of decomposition, or to add chemicals to the food to stop this change. These latter chemicals are the antioxidants.

First, let us consider the chemical modification of fats. The main difference between the composition of animal and vegetable fats is in their 'saturation'. This means the amount of hydrogen present in each fat. The greater the degree to which a product is unsaturated, the less hydrogen it will contain. Animal fats are often completely saturated—that is, they contain as much hydrogen as is chemically possible. These are found in large amounts in fat associated with red meat. They undergo oxidation only slowly, but whilst suitable for energy, their value otherwise for nutrition is limited.

The main fat type in butter and cheese is not completely saturated, but contains a small degree of unsaturation—that is, the amount of hydrogen is reduced slightly from the maximum. These fats do decompose slowly through oxidation, and this explains why butter goes rancid after storage over several weeks or months.

Vegetable oils, such as sunflower or groundnut oil, are much less saturated than the fats in butter. Whilst stored in a fully stoppered bottle, there will be little opportunity for oxygen to interact and cause decomposition. However, once food items have been fried in these oils, there will be opportunity for rapid decomposition. Consider crisps as an example. If these are fried in sunflower oil and stored for some weeks, a rancid taste will develop. To overcome this, the oils—originally of vegetable origin—are treated before cooking with hydrogen to make them more saturated. This results in the formation of fats that are less likely to oxidise to produce unpleasant smells during storage. What in effect has been achieved is the conversion of some polyunsaturated vegetable oils to the more saturated animal fat! The list of ingredients on the packet may state, 'Vegetable oil and hydrogenated vegetable oil.' The consumer, rightly educated to believe that vegetable oils are more desirable than animal fat, is not aware that 'hydrogenated vegetable oil' means in reality animal fat. The use of this chemical trick is aimed at prolonging the storage potential of the product; the adverse effect on nutrients seems hardly to have been considered.

The alternative to this approach is the incorporation into processed food of chemicals that neutralise the chemical reactivity of atmospheric oxygen. This substance can be viewed as providing the food with extra hydrogen so that it, rather than the fat, tends to react with oxygen in the air. As with colourants, these additives are either naturally occurring or artificial. They are added to vegetable oils, sausages, margarine, soups, rice, pork pies, canned meals, biscuits and a host of other processed foods.

A well-known example of a natural antioxidant is Vitamin C or, to give it its correct name, ascorbic acid. This is found naturally in many vegetables and fruits, notably citrus, and would appear to be completely safe. Indeed, some really gigantic doses have been given to patients in an attempt to cure the common cold. Whilst there has been no convincing evidence of benefit from this, there certainly has been no reason to suspect toxicity.

Should we not therefore adopt an attitude towards antioxidants as proposed with colourants—namely, only use naturally-occurring substances in amounts established as being safe? After all, they are used only in processed food to prolong shelf life. The alternative to their use is to obtain food, processed or otherwise, of recent manufacture. Meanwhile the packet term 'hydrogenated vegetable oil' must be clarified so that the consumer understands the practical significance of this group of substances.

Preservatives

There has always been a need for certain foods to be preserved. Many procedures have been well researched and their safety defined by many years of use. These include drying, pickling, canning and deep-freezing. Many of the anxieties over preservatives in food result from their use in perishable products which have been stored for too long. These include pies, soft drinks, fish, frozen pizzas, cakes, processed cheese, sausages, some fruit, bacon and canned hams. It is certainly possible to do without these preservatives altogether. The question whether any of the 35 or more of these permitted chemicals is dangerous cannot be answered with confidence. However, the great majority are entirely synthetic, and there are real concerns over some—the nitrates and nitrites (E249–E252). There is little reason to incriminate the use of nitrates or nitrites themselves in causing toxicity problems. However, there is reason to suspect that chemicals produced from these in the body might be dangerous, and even on occasion cause cancer. This explains the attempts to reduce the amount of nitrates in river and drinking water, where their concentrations are raised because of the excessive use of fertilisers.

Why do we need nitrates and nitrites? These substances appear to be almost unique in their ability to prevent the growth of *Clostridium botulinum*. This can be important for preserving items in vacuum packs, such as bacon, or in canning of hams. Normal canning temperatures achieve about 125°C–130°C and this eliminates all bacteria. Unfortunately, ham fares badly under these conditions, and the use of nitrites permits somewhat lower temperatures.

The use of nitrates and nitrites in bacon, salami, sausages and pies is simply designed for the convenience of the retailer, and perhaps also for the consumer.

The elimination of all these preservatives would have a considerable impact on our shopping habits. Such perishable food could not be stored for weeks in the supermarket for the occasional shopper; it would have to be purchased at frequent intervals, either from supermarkets or from local retail outlets.

Cholesterol

There is still confusion over cholesterol. I shall attempt here to summarise its significance, but the whole story is, unfortunately, more complicated. Cholesterol is a large chemical made up mainly of carbon and hydrogen; it does not dissolve in water and can produce crystals with sharp edges capable of 'damaging' blood vessels such as those in the heart.

The problem with cholesterol is that it is required as a component of structures in all our body cells, or to make hormones. In practice most of our cholesterol is made in the liver, and carried round the body in the blood to the cells where it is used. When in the blood, the cholesterol is enclosed in proteins that enable most of it to dissolve. Any unwanted cholesterol is returned to the liver where it is usually carried out of the body through bile entering our intestines.

If healthy people eat food rich in cholesterol, all that happens is that their own production of it stops, so that the amount in the blood does not increase. A few years ago we fed volunteers the food richest in cholesterol, that is egg yolks, and found that over the next few hours there was no change in the amount of cholesterol in their blood. Unfortunately, a small number of people are unable to carry cholesterol normally in the blood, and if these people eat foods high in cholesterol, it can accumulate with damage to blood vessels. Blood tests can be done to see if a person suffers from this problem; an alternative approach would be to consider whether one's parents and grandparents lived to a ripe old age. If this was the case, then the risk from eating cholesterol would be small, since most of the diseases associated with it run in families.

For reasons not fully understood, saturated fats, such as those found in fatty meat, tend to increase blood cholesterol in many of us. This does not happen with margarine—rich in unsaturated fat. So whilst fat, butter and margarines are all very low in cholesterol itself, it is reasonable dietary advice to eat a considerable portion of fat that is unsaturated. Such desirable foods include margarines and oils made from most vegetable oils, and fish and vegetables as a whole. Unsaturated fats, in addition to lowering blood cholesterol, are also needed for other body functions and are described as essential.

This does not mean that dairy products should necessarily be avoided. Most people can eat diets containing both saturated and unsaturated fats, and probably more important than the exact food is the amount of it. So excessive total fat intake may be as harmful as smoking as far as cholesterol and heart disease are concerned. Dietary roughage and moderate amounts of alcohol seem to be beneficial on the effects of blood cholesterol.

Salt, Sugar, Monosodium Glutamate
Some of the flavour of manufactured food is inevitably lost during the processing. The addition of salt, sugar and monosodium glutamate is intended to restore the appeal. There appears to be a deep-rooted biological attribute of man that desires sweet or salty food, hence the addition of salt and sugar. Monosodium glutamate is the sodium salt of glutamic acid, a naturally occurring component of proteins, and is a fairly non-specific flavour enhancer. These three additives are therefore 'natural'. Are they harmful?

Sugar has been the subject of a great deal of controversy. The issues are, however, fairly simple. The sugar we usually eat is chemically sucrose. This is but one of many carbohydrates in our diet; others include glucose, fructose and starch. None of these is essential, but provides one of the sources of energy. Therefore there is nothing inherently good or bad about sugar; the question, as with fats, is one of the amount eaten. The concern over processed food is that it may contain more sugar than the taste alone suggests.

Salt, and any monosodium glutamate present, comprise a different and much more complicated issue.

The important question over dietary salt is this: is it or is it not safe to eat as much as one wants? It is frequently stated that too much salt will increase the risk of high blood pressure, heart attacks and strokes. But where does the belief that too much salt is bad for you come from? A typical survey might show that people in one country who eat a lot of salt are more likely than low salt eaters to get these problems but does this mean that salt is harmful? The answer to the question is, 'not necessarily'. The high salt eaters might also eat large amounts of fat and starch, both of which in excess are thought capable of causing these diseases. For example, a diet of well-seasoned chips, baked beans and fried eggs, interspersed with cheeseburgers, would provide a great deal of all of them—salt, fat and carbohydrates. It would be impossible to identify any particular food component that was responsible for these diseases.

The other approach is to look at certain medical problems where a high salt diet has been shown to be dangerous, and where cutting down on salt has been beneficial. These do include high blood pressure, kidney and heart disease, although these affect less than one person in twenty in younger age groups. So the medical view seems to be now that, unless you are suffering from one of these conditions that makes eating too much salt dangerous, you can eat salt fairly liberally.

Most people will agree with this philosophy. But the problem for the individual is not solved. How does any person know whether he or she is unable to tolerate a high salt diet? The answer must usually be uncertainty.

For the population as a whole, it therefore makes sense not to eat too much salt. This is yet another argument for preferring whole, unprocessed food, where the natural taste and flavour has not been lost.

Incidentally, lemon or lime are very good flavour enhancers, and can often substitute for salt and monosodium glutamate.

PART III

THE SOLUTION TO THE PROBLEM

14 *The Responsibility for Food Safety*

The ultimate responsibility for food safety still lies with the Minister of Agriculture, Fisheries and Food. Despite numerous calls for the responsibility for food safety to be discharged from this Ministry during the last few years, there has been no change. This must be a deliberate policy of the government since numerous opportunities have presented for responsibility for food safety to be devolved to another body.

Whilst there is much pressure from consumer organisations to take food safety out of MAFF, as to where it should go, the views are not so unanimous. There have been, broadly, three proposals. One is that there should be a Ministry for Food, the second, that the Department of Health should take responsibility, and the third, that there should be an agency independent of the government of the day, but answerable to parliament as a whole. This must be my own preferred option, because of the expectation that a food ministry or the Department of Health could be influenced by food production interests through general government pressures. In the United States, the Food and Drugs Administration (or FDA) fulfils the two roles of food safety and licensing of medicinal drugs. It has been presented as a model agency and probably has been effective and ethical over the years. There are, however, suspicions now of some rather too close relationships with major commercial interests. This type of problem will never disappear completely, whatever the nature of the organisation.

That there has been such a demand for food safety to be excluded from MAFF denotes something is seriously amiss. So let us look at the structure and activity of the Ministry.

MAFF was set up many years ago when there was a national problem of food production and distribution. The responsibility for 'food' was largely a matter of ensuring an adequate food supply to people who might otherwise be malnourished. The problem today, of controlling commercial exploitation of an abundance of food, is quite different. So traditionally, MAFF has always been responsible primarily for food production. The cynical pretence that it now has a prime responsibility to protect the consumer (see White Paper, July 1989) is one of the best examples of 'double speak' in recent times. Let us be quite open about this: MAFF protects the farmers, food processors, large retailers and various related bodies such as pharmaceutical companies.

The Ministry is headed by one Senior Minister and some Junior Ministers. These are elected members of parliament but may not have any real expertise in the many aspects of the subject. The Ministers are the essential fronts to the civil servants, who present the Minister with information which they believe is relevant, as problems arise. The civil servants are not elected, are largely anonymous, and may have very sympathetic views on the commercial exploitation of food.

The commercial pressures applied to MAFF come from the farmers' lobby, particularly the National Farmers' Union, MPs with agricultural constituencies, a relatively small number of farming companies, food processors, and retail chains. Perhaps the number of such influential companies is as few as twenty. It was quite clear that the 1990 Food Safety Bill was converted from what could have been a highly significant piece of legislation to a vague and fairly useless instrument as the result of these pressures.

MAFF is responsible for monitoring, preventing and treating epidemics of disease in food animals and birds. To achieve this, there is a national network of veterinary surgeons, other experts and laboratories, with a centralised collating and administrative unit at Weybridge. This activity is primarily to protect the farming community. If a localised epidemic occurred in an animal or bird, MAFF might initiate a policy of slaughter and containment to prevent spread to uninfected farms. The culling of salmonella-infected chickens has been a departure from the usual policy, in that it is intended, or at least is pretending, to protect the consumer. This policy was introduced as a result of pressure of public opinion and has infuriated the egg men. It remains to be seen for how long the policy will continue: not because it is without justification, but because of damage to the egg industry (see Chapter 4).

To put in a few good words for MAFF. The Ministers, advised by the civil servants, would appear to do their best for the interests of British farmers over European or international issues. This is where the chief responsibility of MAFF should lie.

Where does the Department of Health fit in? Regrettably hardly at all, under considerable influence from MAFF and the government as a whole. The Public Health Laboratory Service (PHLS) is a national network responsible for diagnosing food poisoning, water-borne and other infections. It does some research, but has no executive power and inadequate influence on the government. Each of the regional directors meets the national Director on a regular basis to receive policy information and indoctrination. The Director has a close liaison with the Department of Health, including Junior Ministers. Each regional laboratory is expert in identifying which particular bacterium caused food poisoning. In addition, there is a 'super-expert' laboratory in London, which looks at the small print, and identifies changes in the incidence of food poisoning. But it has no powers to do anything at all about it. The role of the PHLS therefore seems subservient to the Department of Health, itself subservient to the government and MAFF. Between 1983 and 1988, as the food poisoning figures increased, particularly those for salmonella, the PHLS just seemed to watch. Most of its employees are forbidden to have contact with the media, and it now employs a full-time press officer to obstruct the over-inquisitive journalist.

During 1988 there was a series of meetings between the Department of Health, the PHLS and the egg producers over the rising salmonella problem. The disarray seemed complete. The Department of Health warned hospitals about the danger of eggs in August 1988, but only warned the general public in late November of that year because of media pressure.

The Department of Health would be expected to take an active role in the prevention of food poisoning. Occasionally it does, but so many of its activities seem to be in response to crises that should never have happened in the first place. In this country, the absence of adequate regular monitoring of food at the point of sale, and the failure to anticipate problems, have made the department essentially reactive, not proactive.

The senior medical staff at the Department of Health must experience some conflict between their role as executors of government policy and their tacit responsibility to protect the health of the public.

With relevance to both the Department of Health and MAFF, let us consider the function of 'government scientists'. It is clear that there is deep distrust by many members of the public of some alleged scientific advice. The media uses the word 'government scientist' in an ambiguous way. Involvement of scientists with government occurs in a number of ways. Some are fully and exclusively employed by Ministries or Departments. Their functions are broadly two-fold: to provide their own expertise when needed, and to enact government policy. All scientists have their own personal views on matters, and there may be conflict between their personal, or indeed professional, opinion and what is being asked of them.

The very senior scientists, such as the Chief Veterinary Officer at MAFF, or the Chief Scientific Officer at the Department of Health, will usually be well advanced in their careers, and less insecure than their junior colleagues who will in practice have to 'toe the official line'. Even the senior officers, however, have to face the conflict involved in putting the scientific case before the needs of government policy. The penalty for putting the scientific case first could be early retirement and/or loss of a knighthood!

The relationship between the wholly employed government scientists and the media is difficult. Constraints on media comment are usually either formally written into their contracts or are implicit. Any statement to the media is usually made only after consultation with civil servants, and it is difficult to know whether a comment attributed by a ministry spokesperson to an individual or a group of scientists does truly reflect their personal or collective views accurately. The removal of secrecy from these advisory procedures would enable the public to hear the scientists' views at first hand.

Many statements by MAFF, either personally through Ministers or scientists or through press releases, are intended to 'reassure' the public. This is applaudable if there is no real problem, and honest information can be provided that will reassure. But there is increasing cynicism that frequently the overriding intention is to persuade the public all is well even if there is a real problem, so that the problem will not need to be solved, and the commercial activities of the food producers will continue undiminished. It is as if the intent to reassure has become the only public policy of MAFF. If there is a problem, then reassurances for the discerning members of the public will only be achieved by the implementation of relevant control measures. For example, with BSE it was intended to reassure the public that there was no problem at all for human health from eating beef products. Why were measures such as removing the brain also taken? The public is not that stupid! Many scientists have been involved in these spurious reassurances. This must be a major factor in the loss of credibility in expert advice.

Other advice is obtained from those in full-time employment for bodies other than the government. Employers include universities, the Health Service and industry. A number of permanent and *ad hoc* committees feed advice to Ministers through civil servants. Such scientists are not specifically 'government scientists'; however, their views may well be in sympathy with the government since each adviser is carefully vetted before his appointment to an advisory committee.

The crucial appointment is the chairman of each committee, who will have the experience and authority to guide proceedings in the general direction he or she believes it should go (the chairman remains in close contact with civil servants who present to him ministerial policy). Apart from the influence on the initial selection of membership, the conduct and recommendations can be influenced by civil servants within the Department. For example, appointment of retired scientists seems to be a common practice of MAFF. Retired scientists may well be out of touch with research being undertaken elsewhere, and they will find it difficult to keep up with these events. Moreover, they will have few colleagues with whom to exchange views on a day-to-day basis. They will also tend to see problems in the context of how they were some years ago, and may be reluctant to accept the significance of new findings. So retired scientists, whilst possessing ideal and predictable attributes to cope with problems that occurred in the past, may not be best suited to advise on novel problems.

On appointment to advisory committees, many scientists have in the past been asked to comply with the 1911 Official Secrets Act. This Act has been replaced by the 1989 Act which now excludes commercial information. However, other acts do provide strong intimidatory clauses, such as the 1968 Medicines Act, so, in effect, scientists can do little to prevent their views from being misinterpreted. Not all the relevant information about an issue may be provided to members, and where the committee has an inclination to make a decision contrary to the aspiration of the Ministry, the issue comes back time and time again, until (hopefully, from the Ministry's point of view) the correct decision is achieved. This is cynical, and of course such manipulation does not occur in all matters. Many issues, notably those without a substantial commercial inference, are dealt with entirely properly. Some of the experience that has enabled me to make these comments was gained during my membership of the Veterinary Products Committee between 1986 and 1989. This committee advises MAFF on the suitability of drugs in food and other animals.

It is, therefore, certainly possible for a committee, whilst responding to pressures from MAFF and the Department of Health, to produce recommendations that seem to be at variance with the interests of the public as a whole. The recommendation to legalise food irradiation is an important example.

The end result has been growing public scepticism of the judgement of many scientists; this is unfortunate, as the individual members of the committee are generally of high integrity. It is the system, notably the way that advice is sought and promulgated, that is deficient. This is further support for the need of an independent agency working for food safety, which should be beyond the reach of manipulation. Whatever happens, return of confidence in scientific judgement by the public may take some time.

A further problem affecting the availability of truly independent scientists is the progressive cuts in funding of higher education over the last few years. Almost no university or technical college department involved with applied sciences (as opposed to some fundamental molecular work that still has generous central funding) can now survive without grants from industry. Receipt of money from industry may produce no major effects on a department in the short term; in the long term, however, that department is unlikely to publish results harmful to the companies providing its funds. Indeed, over the years, the relationship between industry and the academic department can become extremely close. It is difficult to define now the degree of academic excellence by university departments of 'Food Science'. Some of these departments seem to show a priority in defending malpractices in the food industry, whereas surely they should be challenging these practices and those companies pursuing them.

Research directly funded by MAFF has tended to decline over the years. Presumably the justification for this is that industry should be responsible for its own control. This is clearly unsatisfactory. Marketing policies always seem to dominate safety issues in industry unless legislation forces the need to take safety seriously.

The net results of these changes are that the base for independent research and comment on food safety is now minuscule. Unless this is corrected soon, then there will be little possibility of training scientists in this field in the future.

Who is going to represent the interests of the consumer at the advanced technological level?

Pressure Groups
Food production is very big business and there are numerous pressure groups protecting the interests of the farmer, processor and retailer. Just a few examples are

given below. The most powerful supporter of the farmers is said to be the House of Commons Agriculture Committee who will criticise any deficiency in MAFF or anything or anyone if they impinge on the well-being (that is, the profits) of the farmers. Quite why and how this group of backbenchers with little specific expertise in many of the scientific issues have achieved their over-inflated reputation remains a mystery. They do seek advice from scientists, often retired (see above), but that they can pretend to be able to evaluate the authority of different scientific evidence is quite amazing.

Many distributors and producers of specific food items or components will contribute a small levy to a public relations company aimed at promoting that product and answering any criticism of it by any means possible. Such PR companies may not have any expertise in scientific or medical matters but know the ins and outs of the media. There are some PR companies, however, which do have some particular expertise, that can be used to defend their product. The Meat and Livestock Commission is the PR front of the red meat industry and receives a levy on slaughtered animal turnover. Other bodies range from the Chicken Information Service to the Monosodium Glutamate Information Service (or words to that effect). Companies also exist to defend eggs, tomatoes—indeed almost any product you like to mention. The Chilled Food Association defends chilled food, and it certainly needs to!

Some of the PR outfits give the impression of fairly grandiose organisations. They may in fact be nothing more than a part-time employee with desk and chair.

Six of the main supermarket chains have formed the Food Safety Advisory Centre, fronted by Michael Young.

On the other side, several pressure groups attempt to protect the consumer. The Consumers' Association is much more than a pressure group—whilst its terms of reference relate to the consumer, it provides some excellent in-depth analyses. This means it sees both sides of the debate. Let us hope it does not become too sympathetic to the producers!

Charities, such as Parents for Safe Food, are active campaigners. Tim Lang now works for this charity, having moved from the London Food Commission, another charity. One of the dangers of being effective in this area—that is, reducing the profitability of an industry in order to improve the lot of consumers—is that it generates antagonism. This usually manifests itself in personal offensiveness by those with vested interests, rather than solving the particular problems.

The Guild of Food Writers is an enthusiastic body of sophisticated and knowledgeable journalists intent on presenting the issues accurately. This must have desirable implications for the consumer, although the organisation is not a specific pressure group.

Then, finally, you the consumer can wield power. It is up to you to buy only what you want, to complain over substandard products or meals and to educate your children beyond the daily advertising propaganda for beefburgers and the like.

To put our food supply in order will require effort, money patience, determination and above all, honesty. It will not be achieved overnight. It will also require a philosophy by the government and the public that is different from the morality of the last decade where the primacy of the profit motive has eroded integrity, safety and compassion. A realisation will be required that, despite massive investments of money, some food production systems are inherently unsafe and must be abandoned. Such changes cannot be implemented overnight; however, a future commitment to these changes by the food industry and by the government would go a long way to reassure the public in the short term.

An agency independent of government and food producers must be set up to identify these malpractices and enforce the solutions to the various problems. In farming methods, the greatest single concern is the return of rendered offal to animal feeds. Theoretically, very high temperatures might interrupt this potentially dangerous cycle, although the agents causing spongiform encephalopathies would not be eliminated by any treatment that left useful feed. In practice, short cuts are taken, and it would seem desirable to implement a total ban on any feeding of treated remains to the same or similar species. Ruminants such as cattle or sheep should never have received these products at all.

The intensive rearing of broilers, turkeys, ducks and egg-layers could progressively disappear through the failure to grant planning permission for new factories. It is not generally appreciated that the frequent application of, say, chicken manure to soil has severe disadvantages. Within perhaps ten years, a sourness in the soil makes it unsuitable for cultivation of most plants, except nettles!

It is of course essential that the balance between the availability of free range produce and the demand should be maintained. Presumably price differentials would develop from these pressures.

The phrase 'free range' has generally been used hitherto; this has been intentional, to define the desirable type of husbandry. 'Organic' is often used to indicate rearing conditions, particularly those of the nutrients of crops or animals. Many excellent associations already exist to further 'organic' or 'free range' farming. These are to be applauded. However, the consumer at present has to place her trust entirely in the retailer's description of a product as 'organic'. One function of an independent monitoring agency could be to ensure that the labelling of a product as 'organic' or 'free range' did actually correspond to the farming methods used. This would be most difficult to ensure for products purchased from overseas. Perhaps the shopper will in the future place most trust in British 'organic' or 'free range' produce.

Time and time again, we return to the central requirement for better food—that is, it is up to the consumer to want it, and to purchase it. Governments, farmers, food-processing companies, and retailers can only provide the opportunity for the consumer to make the various choices. Hopefully, the last two or three years have achieved a reawakening of the interest in food, and hopefully, will in the future cause the consumer to give priority to quality and safety of the product, and to environmental and animal welfare issues. Some supermarket chains seem to operate on the assumption that economy and appearance, sometimes of the packet, are the only considerations of their buying public. Let us hope that we shall become more discerning and demand better food.

15 *The Way Forward*

In previous chapters, we have studied the defects in the various parts of the food chain liable to breakdown, mainly from the point of view of safety. We have also seen how certain new technologies, such as food irradiation, *sous vide*, and BST could aggravate the problems rather than confer any real benefit. In this chapter, suggestions will be made for change, and an Appendix follows providing some general notes on available foods, to show that whilst placing most emphasis on the problem areas, we should not forget that some of our food is satisfactory!

The Food Supply

The main venue at which food is purchased is the supermarket. The local retailer, and indeed the whole local or village community, have surrendered to the regional supermarket during the last 30 years. This change has occurred with the full enthusiasm of the buying public; it is not just a question of the big business engulfing the small. Nevertheless, the author believes that the supermarket culture has affected the attitude of the consumer, who in turn seems to demand more of the supermarket produce, rather than consider returning to local retailers, where they still exist.

The first important attribute of the supermarket is the obvious advantage of adequate car parking, to attract the motorist and enable large volumes of goods to be transported home. Next, the range of food items is generally comprehensive. This includes alcoholic drinks, domestic items, pet foods, chemists' paraphernalia and so on. There is no need to shop anywhere else for food and domestic items. The supermarket is so organised that the purchaser can select as many items as possible within a finite time. The shelves are open, even though this is clearly unsatisfactory for refrigerated items. The large number of items deposited in the trolleys require tough packaging to avoid squashing—hence one main reason for the ludicrous waste of packaging materials, many of which are not biodegradable. The check-out can sometimes cause a delay, but most companies are speeding up this procedure. Thus the supermarket enables many and varied items to be purchased in as short a time as possible. This means that instead of shopping almost daily, as was required in the past, only one shopping expedition is required weekly or even fortnightly. This in a way flatters the shopper: it is saying to him or her, 'You are too important a person and have too many other more useful activities to do to waste unnecessary time on shopping.' And then the final seduction of the supermarket—the price. Generally, the prices are lower, often substantially, than in local shops. Incidentally, one important aspect of price where research is needed is to look at the total net cost per person or family of either supermarket or locally purchased food. The reason for this doubt is that bulk purchasing of perishable goods from the supermarket might generate substantially more waste than careful and frequent purchasing of smaller amounts of more expensive items locally.

Many of our problems with the food chain are determined by the supermarket/consumer interface. If attempts are made to identify responsibility for these problems, the food industry can quite reasonably state that it is responding to consumer demand. It also follows that, if we wish to see changes, it will be the responsibility of consumers to create new demands. This is already happening on selected items, such as the demand for organic vegetables and free range meat products.

The first set of problems facing the supermarket culture is the need for each shop to stock a comprehensive selection of available items. Many of these products are only occasionally demanded by the customer. This can generate major strategic problems for perishable items. If it is assumed that the total monthly volume of sales of a product, such as crisps, is more or less constant, then, generally, the more different types of product that there are available, the less of any one type will be sold per day. In order to maintain the viability of this activity, it means either increasing the interval of delivery of each item to be in smaller consignments, or storing each product for longer. If the latter occurs, then problems of quality or safety may not be met. Take crisps again. Those which are fried in pure vegetable oil that is high in polyunsaturated fatty acids will not last on the shelf as long as those fried with saturated animal fat. The reason is that there is a natural tendency for the polyunsaturated fatty acids to decompose on storage to produce 'off' flavours (see Chapter 13). The message is beginning to become clear: more choice does not mean better quality; it could well result in a deterioration.

Consider another set of items—branded cakes, pastries and various baked products. The consumer knows these well and requires to purchase his or her favourite at the supermarket. Each branded item has somehow to be distributed at regular intervals to each supermarket in the country. This requires massive centralised production facilities, fleets of lorries and vans, and intermediary staging posts that can supply a group of supermarkets with a series of products. The supermarkets' 'own' brands (which may be some of these other products re-labelled) also have to be treated in this way. It is no wonder that our roads are choked with mobile manufactured food. Crisps, and baked products are inherently safe because of their low water content, although caution must be exercised with some of the pastry and cake fillings.

The worry comes from the use of central production/ distribution/staging posts/distribution/storage for items which are manifestly perishable. These include some dairy products, pâtés, cooked meats, chilled convenience meals, salamis, pork pies, pasties, sausage rolls, composite salads, coleslaws—indeed almost all the items on the chilled shelves. The concern over the excessive use of preservatives over recent years has largely been stimulated by their need in this type of product as seemingly demanded by the customer. In the absence of preservative, and particularly in the presence of inadequate refrigeration, this type of product is simply not appropriate for the supermarket culture.

It has been suggested that many of the problems with the food chain are accountable by the consumer/supermarket interface. The main pressure is the continued downward pressure on prices, so difficult to escape from, considering how important food items are in the calculation of the retail price index. Would there have been pressures on farmers to use cheap animal protein supplements from the rendering plants without the need for the lowest retail prices? Why are most eggs not labelled with the exact farm of origin? During the last two years, many people have requested that eggs be so identified in order to track down possible food-poisoning sources. The supermarkets have, seemingly, resisted this, so that they can purchase the cheapest possible eggs, including those from abroad, without the customer being aware of their source. Do the supermarkets apply pressure on the manufacturers of processed food to produce the cheapest, and not necessarily the safest product?

Before making some suggestions for change in our food chain, it is first worth pointing out where supermarkets succeed—and succeed well. This is in the provision of non-perishable food, where variety, safety and choice of different sizes of items are commendable. Such items include canned food, deep-frozen food (as long as it is stored correctly), pickled items, preserves and dried foods, including biscuits. Some fruit and vegetables are also of a high quality. With this the main cause of deterioration may be unnecessarily long holding in the home. Ideally, vegetables should be sold at local shops and purchased fairly frequently.

Proposals for the Future
Following on from the above, the first proposal is that non-perishable foods should continue to be available at supermarkets. There will be few problems for the weekly or fortnightly shopper and there will be available a good variety of basic commodities at economical prices. Of the more radical recommendations, the chilled shelves (not the deep-freeze cabinets) should go; produce stored on them, including fresh meat, poultry, fish, dairy products, cooked meats, pâtés, convenience chilled composite foods, and some vegetables, should be the domain of the local retailer. So, too, should cakes, pastry goods, and bread. Local manufacturers could make a comprehensive range of these items, and supply nearby groups of retailers, and these would replace the senseless plethora of branded goods around the country.

For these changes to occur, we, the consumers, must want them to happen and local retailers may have to adopt opening hours found on the continent to serve the working wife or husband or single person. It is notable that Asian communities in West Yorkshire, and presumably elsewhere, already do aspire to this.

Some local shops tend to stock items for too long because of the lack of demand. It is hoped that these exhortations will increase their throughput so that the produce is truly 'fresh'.

Already, consumer pressures are mounting against the purchase of intensively reared meat. This will continue, and it should be possible for the United Kingdom to be self-sufficient in food without the need for intensive rearing at all. Presumably if we (a) replaced some of our meat rations with vegetable food, (b) ate a little less food altogether, and (c) did not waste so much food, the savings would be sufficient to purchase quality meat and poultry, reared and processed under ideal conditions.

Whether these changes will occur, and on what scale, is largely up to the consumer and local entrepreneurs. Do not expect the government of the day or the major food-producing and selling firms to show any enthusiasm for them!

So, in the final analysis, it is up to all of us to make the decision to purchase and eat food of high quality. It is certainly possible to flourish on a purely vegetarian diet which would provide some advantages for reducing environmental pollution and for dispelling disquiet over animal welfare. One of the potential problems with vegetarian food, however, is that the quality can deteriorate after preparation and storage, whether frozen or chilled. It is not surprising that reheated meals on British Rail or on aeroplanes are often ruined by the poor quality of the vegetable components.

Whether or not one is a vegetarian, the case for types of food other than reheated meals is surely overwhelming. Perhaps deep down the British citizen has an expectation of three hot meals each day, with the latter two comprising 'meat and two veg'. That we expect this food wherever we are and at precisely predetermined times may be an important factor in explaining the poor quality of so much of our institutional and transport food.

Another point to consider when eating out is whether the food is freshly prepared or has been reheated. Most takeaway restaurants do not permit the waiting customer to see how the food is prepared. However, some do, notably pizza houses and of course fish and chip restaurants. The latter are probably top of the safety league, and can certainly produce items of good quality. Sometimes beef dripping is used—this is particularly popular in Yorkshire. Elsewhere, vegetable oils are used, and if these are replenished regularly there should be few problems. If anyone is concerned about the source of the fat or oil, then they should ask!

Indeed, customers in restaurants should be encouraged to show greater curiosity over their food, and to complain if it is not up to expectation. Consider an item such as a jacket potato. It could have been cooked by any of the following procedures. First, it could have been cooked entirely in a conventional oven. Next it could have been previously oven-baked then reheated in a microwave to order, or it could be cooked first in a microwave, then finished in an oven, or be entirely microwaved. The end result will vary enormously, with the potato from the conventional oven being crisp and fragrant, and that from the microwave being limp and tasteless.

Generally, the greater the speed of service, the more likelihood that the meal has been prepared in advance and then reheated. Impatience with food seems a particularly British and North American attitude. In several continental countries, the longer wait is thought to be fully justified by the quality of the resultant meal. Perhaps, of rapidly available meals, the pizza prepared and cooked entirely on site is the most rewarding.

In many ways, the problems of our food are self-inflicted. We seem to desire in the United Kingdom an endless selection of composite food items that require no effort or time in preparation. It is as if the British character has changed to becoming impatient, greedy and selfish. Were we not once dogged, and determined to pursue enduring goals? This was not intended as a book on morals, but the food industry has claimed, with a certain amount of truth, that it produces what the consumer wants. However, it could also be argued that the food industry, with cunning marketing and packaging ploys, tells the consumer to want what it can produce at greatest profit!

So the message is simple: seek high quality and genuinely fresh whole food, be it organic or free range. Enjoy the art of manipulation of food and the creation of your meals. The meal at home should be the central celebration of the family or friends or just yourself. It deserves more status than ready-prepared dinners gulped down during the television commercial breaks.

APPENDIX

Available Foods—
Buying, Storing, Cooking

The following notes on individual food items are presented partly to enthuse over some, partly to admonish the suppliers (while it is awful to say so, it may be the consumer who wants or accepts these products) and partly to point out avoidable dangers.

Bread

The upsurge in recent years in loaves made with natural or organic unbleached flour has been gratifying. The salt content needs watching, and of extreme annoyance to me is the non-availability of unsliced loaves. Surely anyone can slice bread to the thickness desired. Most ready-sliced bread makes very thick sandwiches. Perhaps of greater concern is the fact that a sliced loaf can go stale much more quickly, with loss of water from each cut surface, whereas an old unsliced loaf can be rejuvenated by cutting and discarding the end slice! Remember, too, that home-made bread is delicious, even if it has not risen properly!

On the subject of sandwiches, the fashion for purchasing made-up sandwiches is quite extraordinary. Think about this.

Potatoes

The range of potatoes in many outlets is greater than ever; they come loose, bagged, old, new, dirty, clean, pink, brown, etc., etc. Potatoes are an excellent food, and my only complaint is that some of those purporting to be 'new' are not. Small, clean, white potatoes that have been imported some weeks previously are not 'new'. It can be difficult to obtain real new potatoes even when seasonal. Locally grown produce, distributed through local retailers, would provide the answer.

Vegetables

The quality of vegetables in supermarkets is so variable that it is dangerous to generalise. Perhaps the greatest problem is the expectation by the consumer that every class of vegetable will be available every week of the year. To achieve this, many have to be imported. These deteriorate largely through drying, and their quality would definitely not be helped by irradiation. To withstand the rigours of prolonged transport, many vegetables are presented in plastic boxes, surely unacceptable environmentally.

Storage of vegetables in the home can present a problem. They need not be stored in the refrigerator, and in any case there may not be room. A cool room or cellar would be ideal but these are rare features in modern housing. So they end up wilting in the hot kitchen. The message once more is to purchase them as frequently as you can, when you need them.

The fashion for boxes containing chopped vegetables, salads, sometimes with fruits and nuts, sometimes sauced, as with coleslaw, is quite extraordinary. The worrying aspects of these are that you cannot wash each item, the product may be many days old before you buy it, and unless consumed very quickly a few tattered or brown lettuce leaves can give a poor image. And, of course, there is more plastic. If you do buy these products, store them in the refrigerator for not more than two days.

Mayonnaise, Salad Creams, etc.

Traditionally, vinegar has been the preservative used to prevent contamination of these, but with the vogue for reduction in additives and preservatives some of these products may contain insufficient vinegar to prevent the growth of bacteria which accidentally contaminate the product after opening. For this reason, even if the label does not state so, the bottle or jar should be kept refrigerated after opening, preferably for not more than two days. This could result in waste, but why has the concentration of vinegar been reduced since vinegar is harmless? Or why not try making a home-made dressing? Shake up equal volumes of walnut oil and vinegar to which you have added a little mustard, sugar and herbs, such as chopped mint. It is safe; it will keep for ages, it is excellent nutritionally and is very economical (this is the only recipe in the book!).

Fresh Fruit

As with vegetables, the quality of fruit varies enormously according to outlet. I know of some where the range and condition of each product is excellent. There is also no need to use irradiation here. However, with centralised buying and long distribution times to peripheral supermarkets, some drying, wrinkling and browning can occur. The answer to these problems is not to attempt always to stock 'out of season' products and to use local retail outlets.

Dried Food, Gravies, Custards, Soups, etc.

These are certainly safe in the dried state. Most are prepared by large-scale freeze-drying which causes any bacteria present to go into 'suspended animation'. So when soup or gravy is made up and kept warm, there is a risk that these bacteria will 'wake up' and start growing. They are not likely to do so for one-and-a-half to two hours, so this really is the safe maximum time for these at room temperature. It is a good general rule only to make up enough for the actual meal.

Bean Sprouts

These deserve special mention because, despite being vegetables, they are liable to contamination with enormous numbers of bacteria. Indeed, a major salmonella

outbreak has been caused by them. Therefore, if you find a
need to eat bean sprouts, wash them very thoroughly. Do
not be reassured by the cleanliness of the outside
wrappings!

Fish

My favourite food! Even if nominally rather expensive if
based on a weight price, it is excellent value for the
nutrition, flavour, and sheer pleasure of eating. The high
unsaturated fatty content fortunately makes it a poor
candidate for cook-chilling. The choice is therefore usually
fresh in the true sense (that is, uncooked—about one to
three days from catching—hopefully) or deep frozen. In
other countries dried and raw fish are eaten. The former
must surely be of inferior quality compared to the real
item, and the latter of doubtful safety. Brief cooking only is
usually required for safety. However, there seems a
tendency to present some types, particularly smoked
varieties, in vacuum packs. These have been discussed in
Chapter 7 and are not recommended. Regrettably, the days
of door-step delivery of fresh fish have largely gone, as
have those of many local fishmongers. The supermarket
stall is often an apology for the real monger. Deep-frozen
fish can be surprisingly, and gratifyingly, of good final
quality, although by weight the actual fish content of
coated items is lower than might be expected. The fish
fingers made into real fish configurations are really
amusing. Frozen fish makes an excellent convenience
meal, and is one of the food industries' major
achievements. The only doubts about fish concern the
artificially farmed salmon and trout, which need a wide
range of drugs during cultivation (see Chapter 13).

Poultry

It will already be obvious that we should consider the
mass-produced, intensively reared chickens, turkeys and
ducks as inferior food. The genuine free range products

are preferable, but a little more expensive. One of the problems that urgently requires a solution is a means of establishing the certainty that the so-called free-range product really has been reared under true free range conditions.

As a result of rearing conditions, slaughtering and preparation methods, we have to assume that most raw poultry is contaminated with some salmonella, campylobacter and listeria. The product can still, however, be managed safely. Four simple rules should be adopted: (1) Keep each poultry product individually wrapped. (2) Keep it separate in the refrigerator from other items, preferably below them. (3) Prepare it—washing, chopping, etc.—on an isolated worktop in the kitchen, and clean up carefully afterwards. (4) Cook it thoroughly. For example, with roasting of whole birds, stuffing is best cooked alongside in a tray, and with barbecues and microwaves you have real problems. The safest solution is first to cook the product conventionally, slowly and thoroughly.

Lamb and Pork
These should not present any particular problems. Treat the raw meat as chicken. If mince is required, there is no reason why lamb or pork cannot be minced, and I suggest that you make your own from whole meat items, so that you and your family and guests know what is in it! Sausages, pies and processed meat products may contain unsaleable parts of almost any animal and are not recommended.

Beef
Beef cannot be recommended since it is not known whether the agent causing BSE can infect man. An exception to this rule might be meat from a definite BSE-free source. This does not include herds in the United Kingdom which have not suffered a BSE case, because animals can be infected but not showing signs of illness

(see Chapter 6). In practice this might mean buying overseas produce. Even here there are problems because the major component on the European beef mountain is unwanted British beef.

Convenience Meals

These seem to offer a straightforward solution for the working cook! But there are many other ways of producing a nutritious and appealing meal quickly. It need not even be hot. Of the convenience meals, those presented at room temperature, often with an expiry date several months ahead, have been subjected to the canning process and are inherently safe, if not exciting.

Deep-freezing arrests bacterial growth, and those from the freezer should be as safe as they were on being frozen. They therefore present fewer problems than the chilled meals which, as discussed in Chapter 7, can be dispensed with easily.

Dairy Products

Conventional butter and margarine should pose no safety problems, but be wary of the low fat products produced by dispersing water into the fat. This water can enable certain bacteria to grow, so keep these products particularly cold (0°C–3°C), ideally for not more than two days.

Yogurt should be safe, on account of its high acidity, as long as nothing silly has been put into it—as occurred with the botulism from the hazelnut purée in 1989. However, if yogurt is stored for too long or at too high a temperature, contamination can be a problem, so note the instructions.

Cheeses, notably hard cheeses, are another recommended and versatile product and they are best stored cool, and not too cold. However if you cannot keep them cool—say 10°C–15°C then the refrigerator is the only answer. Keep each cheese carefully wrapped and when buying soft cheeses, buy those that are whole, loosely wrapped in an impermeable cover in a rigid wooden box. The French know what they are doing with cheeses. There is still a small risk from listeria from these, and those who are worried, or ill, or elderly or pregnant are advised to keep to hard cheeses. My own favourites are white Cheshire for cooking, Wensleydale or Coverdale.

Canned Food

These are still useful in reserve. The canning process destroys all germs except, unfortunately, that causing BSE and the like. If the can is not bulging, the seams not apart, there are no major dents or rusting, canned items should be as safe as any food. It you have a determination to use your microwave, transferring the contents of a can to a plastic or china receptacle creates no problems, and will be much cheaper than the dedicated microwavable meals prepared and sold in plastic dishes.

Further Reading

DEALLER, S. F., and LACEY, R. W. (1990). 'Transmissible Spongiform Encephalopathies: the threat of BSE to man'. To be published in *Food Microbiology*, late 1990/early 1991.

DEPARTMENT OF HEALTH AND SOCIAL SECURITY (1970). *Precooked frozen foods.* HMSO.

DEPARTMENT OF HEALTH AND SOCIAL SECURITY (1980). *Guidelines on pre-cooked chilled foods.* HMSO.

DEPARTMENT OF HEALTH (1989). *Chilled and Frozen. Guidelines on cook-chill and cook-freeze catering systems.* HMSO.

DIEHL, J. F. (1990). *Safety of Irradiated Foods.* Marcel Dekker, Basel.

DRUCE, CLARE (1989). *Chicken and Egg. Who pays the price?* Green Print.

EPSTEIN, S. S. (1989). 'BST: the public health hazards'. *The Ecologist*, 19, 191-5.

HAYES, P. R. (1985) *Food Microbiology and Hygiene.* Elsevier, London.

LANCET (1990). 'Prion disease—Spongiform encephalopathies unveiled'. 336, 21-2.

NORTH, R., and GORMAN, T. (1990). *Chickengate.* Institute of Economic Affairs, London.

RICHMOND, M. H. (1990). *The Microbiological Safety of Food.* Part 1, HMSO.

SOUTHWOOD, R. (1989). *Report of the Working Party on bovine spongiform encephalopathy.* HMSO.

TYRRELL, D. (1989). *Consultative Committee on research into spongiform encephalopathies.* HMSO.

WEBB, T., and LANG, T. (1990) *Food Irradiation. The myth and the reality.* Thorson, London.

INDEX